Behavioral Genetics

An introduction to how genes and environments
interact through development to shape differences
in mood, personality, and intelligence

BY CATHERINE BAKER

*A tool to inform public discussion of
behavioral genetic research
and its broader social implications*

Prepared for a project conducted by the
American Association for
the Advancement of Science
and The Hastings Center

AAAS

ADVANCING SCIENCE, SERVING SOCIETY

THE
HASTINGS
CENTER

For Carolyn, my genetic equivalent

Printed in the United States of America

ISBN 0-87168-697-X

Copyright 2004
American Association for the
Advancement of Science
Directorate for Science &
Policy Programs
1200 New York Ave., NW
Washington, D.C. 20005

Layout and cover design by
AAAS Publication Services.

Additional copies of this report
are available from:
AAAS Scientific Freedom,
Responsibility and Law Program
1200 New York Avenue, NW
Washington, D.C. 20005, USA
Telephone: USA +1-202-326-6606
Fax: USA +1-202-289-4950
E-mail: kallema@aaas.org
Web: www.aaas.org/spp/bgenes/

This report is also available on the Web:
http://www.aaas.org/spp/bgenes/
publications.shtml

Preparation and publication of this volume was supported by a grant from the National
Human Genome Research Institute (RO1 HG001873) and by contributions to the
AAAS Fund for Excellence designated for the Directorate for Science & Policy Programs.

TABLE OF CONTENTS

NOTE: *Words contained in the glossary/index are* blue *where they first appear in Chapters 1 through 7.*

Preface

Behavioral geneticists aim at no less than showing us how genes help to explain why we behave the way we do. One big reason they do their work is that understanding why we behave the way we do is inherently interesting. The second big reason is that they hope their work eventually will lead to curing behavioral disorders as different as alcoholism and schizophrenia. Today they are far from understanding how genes influence those behaviors, but that is their goal.

One might think that such a fascinating field would by now have spawned many brief introductions for lay readers. But that hasn't happened. Part of the explanation for this gap is that the science is complicated. Part of the explanation is that the subject matter of behavioral genetics—mental disease, personality, intelligence—is controversial. Moreover, in the past, research in behavioral genetics has been used to support hateful prejudices, and so perhaps this has led many otherwise-interested writers to steer clear of the topic.

The process that led to this book was started in 1999 as part of a project to explore ideas for improving the public's understanding of behavioral genetics and to fill the void described above. A series of meetings brought together genetic researchers, social scientists, lawyers, and ethicists. Participants shared their knowledge of the science and together explored the question, "What does the public need to know to understand and talk about behavioral genetics?" An experienced writer (not a scientist) listened, asked questions, took notes, and read the papers contributed by participants for another project product, a scholarly volume. Then she started drafting this book, which was subsequently reviewed at several stages by project participants. The result is, we think, a work that is both instructive and a delight to read.

Each chapter begins with a fictional but plausible anecdote about an individual with a question that has to do with behavior. These anecdotes set the genetic science into a real world context. They start readers thinking about basic questions such as, How do behavioral geneticists study the connection between genes and behavior? Can those studies tell me anything about why I act the way I do? Can they tell me anything about the chances that I can make my child do well or badly in life? And so forth. With the story as the hook, readers are pulled into each chapter, where they are introduced to the scientific concepts that can help answer the fictional character's question.

Writing about behavioral genetics is like building a structure on shifting sands. Each day, new discoveries are being made, previously heralded claims are being revised, and new paradigms for the relationship between genes and behavior are being proposed. For example, as this book explains in Chapter 2, the human genome used to be compared to a codebook, a book of life, or an encyclopedia. But today scientists recognize that the genome is much more dynamic than any kind of book and so new metaphors are being tried out — metaphors that may or may not stick with time, depending on what researchers learn next.

Despite the difficulty of capturing a fast-moving subject, we believe this text succeeds as an introduction to the field. It should help readers obtain a firm grounding in the basic science and the tools used by researchers to explore the contribution of the genes (and their essential counterpart, the environment) to behavior. Readers should come away with a vocabulary for discussing the science and with a sense of what genetic science can tell us and do for us, and what its limitations are.

This text describes the promise of — and the problems with — the complex science of behavioral genetics in a way that should be accessible to a broad audience, from high school and college students with an interest in science to the educated lay person whose family may be experiencing events similar to those portrayed in the book's stories. If you want to see where the fascinating and sometimes controversial science of behavioral genetics is headed in the 21st century, you've come to the right place.

As the lead investigators for the larger project, we are indebted to the staff at the Ethical, Legal and Social Implications Research Program at the National Human Genome Research Institute, especially Joy Boyer and Elizabeth Thomson, for their generous support of our work (RO1 HG001873). We are also deeply grateful to Elving Anderson for, at every step of this project, giving so generously of his time and knowledge, as well as to the many project participants (listed on page 131) who contributed their expertise to the preparation of this volume. Finally, we thank Catherine Baker for her tireless work to understand and then describe for you the work of behavioral genetics.

If you would like to read the special supplement of the Hastings Center Report, which summarizes the findings of the project that produced this introduction to behavioral genetics, or you would like to learn more about the volume of essays for advanced students and scholars, please visit our website at http://www.aaas.org/spp/bgenes, where this volume is also available.

Erik Parens   Mark S. Frankel   Audrey R. Chapman
The Hastings Center   AAAS   AAAS

Introduction

Why do humans range so widely in their susceptibility to mental illness, in their willingness to take risks, and in their performance on intelligence tests? One answer to this question comes from scientists in the field of behavioral genetics. They say that the variation in behavioral traits across a population is due, in part, to the genes. So many studies have pointed to connections between genes and particular behaviors that most scientists now feel comfortable stating that there is such a link for every possible behavior.

But what does it really mean to say that there is a link between genes and behavior? Does it mean that there is a gene that makes some of us blush when embarrassed; that there is one gene that makes you prefer classical music and another gene that makes you dislike it; that there is a bunch of genes that each provides for different levels of skill in playing poker? The answer to all these questions is no. Does it mean behavior passes down from generation to generation, i.e., is inherited, just like baldness and eye color? Again, the answer is no.

So when next you see an article that proclaims, "Gene for *[insert a human behavior here]* discovered," read it with a critical eye. Or when you next hear someone say, "He inherited his *[insert a human behavior here]* from his father," receive that with skepticism, too.

The pervasive role of genes in behavior does *not* mean what it is commonly misunderstood to mean. It does not mean that a gene or even several genes can make you act in any particular way. It does not mean that a behavior can "pass down through the genes." Such claims are *not* accepted in behavioral genetics.

It *does* mean that genes play a vital role in the body's development and physiology, and it is through the body, acting in response to and upon surrounding environments, that behavior manifests itself. So while we do inherit our genes, we do not inherit behavior traits in any fixed sense. The effect of our given set of genes on our behavior is entirely dependent upon the context of our life as it unfolds day to day.

Nonetheless, we have tended to assign the genes a grander role. Perhaps one reason why we tend to inflate the role of genes in behavior is that there is no good verb to use when talking about them. It's clearly wrong to say that genes *control* behavior. We might instead say that genes *influence* behavior, that genes *impinge* upon behavior, that genes *are implicated* in behavior, or that they *help instigate* the cellular activity through which behavior is executed. None of these constructions are quite right, either.

It is very difficult to capture in a single verb the gene-behavior relationship, because the way in which genes relate to behavior is complex, indirect, and highly nuanced. It is contingent upon events inside and outside the body — such as diet and features of upbringing — and it is modulated over time. If you keep all these things in mind, it can help you think more coherently about the questions that naturally arise, such as:

- Is our potential predetermined at conception?
- Are we powerless to control our thoughts and actions?
- Will our children turn out a certain way no matter how we raise them?

The answer to each of these questions is once again a resounding *no*. Genes are not enough. They have little predictive power at the level of the individual and they do not override the many other influences on behavior. In fact, it's fair to claim the following statement, though it is unproven and probably unprovable:

> *Based on your genes, no one can say what kind of human being you will turn out to be or what you will do in life.*

If you can only learn one thing about behavioral genetics, that statement should be it. But if you would like to obtain a more sophisticated and deeper understanding of this subject, please read the rest of this book. You will find straightforward definitions of genes and environments. You will learn how genes operate *within* a sensitive and complicated network involving other DNA elements and proteins and *in* specific environments *throughout* the development of an individual. You will gain an understanding of how behavioral genetic research is conducted, particularly in regard to three topics that have been the focus of much of the research in this field: mood disorders, impulsivity, and intelligence. Finally, you will be introduced to the ways in which behavioral genetic research can affect individuals and society at large.

If you read this book, you also will learn about some of the contentious debates that surround behavioral genetics. Scholars argue about the quality of the field's research methods. They disagree about the significance of findings. They question whether the benefits from behavioral genetic research will outweigh the drawbacks.

This last concern stems in part from this field's historic connection to eugenics. This was a doctrine, first emerging in the late 1800's, which held that some people are innately superior due to their genes and therefore those persons should reproduce more than others. Eugenic policy became official practice in many countries, ranging from involuntary sterilization of those deemed unfit in the U.S. and other countries to mass murder of those deemed unsuitable in Nazi Germany. After World War II, overtly eugenic attitudes were forced underground. Nonetheless, there are people today who continue to manipulate and sensationalize science, consciously or subconsciously, to justify social inequities and prejudices.

Many people fear that preliminary and unconfirmed studies, unwarranted conclusions, and misinterpreted data from behavioral genetic research will be used to support modern eugenic policies that maintain privilege and unfairness. They worry that findings from behavioral genetic research will be manipulated to promote prejudice, spread discrimination, invade privacy, and foster unequal treatment under the law. They also worry that as a genetically based definition of normal human behavior advances, the range of socially acceptable human behavior will shrink.

On the other hand, many people are frustrated by so-called "hand-wringing Jeremiahs" who dwell on the problems that could potentially emerge from behavioral genetic research. The people with this view assert that behavior is a worthy avenue of exploration. They believe that studying the genes is one way — one way among many — to learn about behavior. They think that the acquisition of knowledge is good, even knowledge about something as personal and revealing as our own behavior. Indeed, they believe that such knowledge could improve the lives of individuals as well as humanity at large. They acknowledge that the scientific methodology in behavioral genetics is imperfect, but no more so than in any other relatively new field of exploration. Though they share concern about the misuse of information from behavioral genetics, they believe that the pursuit of this knowledge offers more advantages than disadvantages.

This book is the product of a project that brought together advocates and skeptics. The partners in this project share the conviction that an informed public understanding of the principles of genetic science and behavioral research can be an antidote against premature and faulty claims and the misapplication of findings. Our intent with this book is to help non-scientists like yourself gain a better understanding of concepts and terms in behavioral genetics. This education can help you better evaluate what you read and hear about behavioral genetics. It can help you become your own judge of information. And to some extent, it might help you better understand your own behavior.

Acknowledgements

This book results from a four-year project of The Hastings Center and the American Association for the Advancement of Science. The subject of this project was "Tools for Public Conversation about Behavioral Genetics." Early on, project participants decided that a useful tool to foster conversation would be an easy-to-read primer on behavioral genetic research for an audience of interested nonscientists.

The text was shaped by the papers presented and discussions that took place at five meetings of the project's working group and a final conference that was open to the public. Project participants are listed on page 131. My thanks go to each of them.

I am particularly indebted to the following persons who provided specific comments on, and corrections to, parts of this manuscript at various stages in its development: Elving Anderson, Jon Beckwith, Greg Carey, Troy Duster, Marcus Feldman, Mark S. Frankel, Irving I. Gottesman, and John Loehlin. Special acknowledgement goes to Elving, who answered many questions and served as coach, and to Irving, who constantly brought relevant articles to my attention and who was helpfully specific in his suggestions for the text. I give tremendous thanks to Lee Ehrman, who reviewed the entire manuscript with a very sharp scientific and editorial eye, and to Kenneth Schaffner, who also conducted a thorough critique of the whole draft.

Members of the project's management team gave me valuable support through this long writing project: Audrey Chapman, Mark S. Frankel, Erik Parens, Nancy Press, and Elving. I also am grateful to designer Beth Elzer at AAAS; she did a fine job with an unwieldy set of computer files and an anxious writer. Kevin Alleman, Christine Bellordre, Bryn Lander, Clinton Musil, and Kathy Fishback, members of AAAS staff, also provided valuable assistance in the production of this volume.

Peter Wehrwein, a science writer and long-time friend, helped me many times with advice, telephone tutorials, and useful bits of information. Carolyn Reser helped me track down a most elusive fact — the name of the Ray Bradbury story mentioned in Chapter 3.

I relied on two textbooks as valuable references — Greg Carey's *Human Genetics for the Social Sciences* and *Behavioral Genetics* by Robert Plomin *et al*. I also am beholden to the many genetics glossaries on the web – especially to the "gene definitions" and the "SNPs and other genetic variations" glossaries at the website of the Cambridge Healthtech Institute. Finally, I must acknowledge my huge debt to Google.com, which helped me track down in an instant relevant articles, loose facts, bibliographic details, and definitions.

Although many people have guided me on this project, I assume all responsibility for errors and out-of-date information, and for any sections in which I failed to make things clear.

Catherine Baker
September 2003, Bethesda, Maryland

chapter one

■ ■ ■ Margaret, an ambitious mother

Margaret and her husband do not make a lot of money and they do not save much, but she's come up with a grand scheme to make her family wealthy. She's going to turn her two-year-old daughter Cassandra into a professional golfer.

She knows all about Tiger Woods, the golf prodigy who was coached and managed by his father and who has amassed millions of dollars in prize money and endorsements. The incomes of today's professional women's golfers are far below that of Tiger Woods, but Margaret figures that the earning potential of female golfers is bound to increase dramatically in the years ahead.

Margaret played on her college team and probably could have turned professional if she had been given the encouragement she plans to give her daughter. Though her husband's sport of choice is baseball, he too has physical talent that he has probably passed on to his little girl.

Margaret has bought Cassandra a pint-size set of golf clubs so they can start practicing. Of course at her age, Cassandra prefers to use the putter for knocking off the heads of dandelions or beating up anthills. Nonetheless, her mother thinks it should not be difficult as Cassandra gets older to get her to focus on the game.

Margaret figures that with the natural athletic abilities that run in the family, strenuous coaching, careful planning, and a little luck, she should be able to get Cassandra into the pro circuit within fifteen to twenty years. She has not told her husband about this plan yet. She knows just what he'll say: Are you crazy? But if her daughter has innate physical abilities and those abilities are nurtured, directed, and promoted, success is almost assured. Isn't it?

Defining behavior

Seers, prophets, and astrologers of ancient times have tried to predict behavior. Writers such as Shakespeare and Jane Austen have tried to describe it. Freud, Jung, and other psychiatrists have sought to explain it. Today's advice columnists assume they understand it, ministers sermonize about it, and some daytime TV talk show hosts provoke their guests into the worst of it. Yet much of behavior remains a mystery.

It's the unusual person (the differently *behaving* person) who has not tried to understand his or her own behavior or the behavior of others. Therefore, it should come as no surprise that many scientists choose to study behavior.

All living organisms, not just humans, behave. Animals behave, insects behave, and single-celled amoebas behave. Even

Genes were unknown in Shakespeare's time, yet his writing reveals an uncanny, intuitive understanding of human behavior.

plants behave. For example, when a plant turns its leaves toward a source of light, it is behaving. The opposite is also true: things that are not alive do not behave. Rocks and oceans and planets do not behave.

Behaviors are the actions a creature makes, as a whole, in response to the world around it. When an owl swoops down to catch a mouse or when children chase a soccer ball, these are behaviors. Behaviors also are holistic responses to stimuli from inside the body. When your hands begin to tremble and you feel agitated and hyper-alert after your fourth cup of coffee, that is behavior, too.

Mostly, we think of behavior as something conscious such as when we choose to eat a piece of cherry pie. But behavior also can be unconscious, automatic, or instinctual. Talking in your sleep is a behavior, because it is the mind responding to events that occurred while awake. A sneeze is a behavior, because it is the body's response to pollen in the air. The lizard that crawls out from under a rock to bask in the sun is behaving, even though we do not think lizards have a consciousness as human beings do.

Physical manifestations of most diseases are behaviors, too. When a man has an epileptic seizure or when a woman with uncontrolled diabetes falls unconscious, they display behavior despite the fact that they are not in conscious control of their actions.

Some behaviors are uniform across a

whole species such as the way bears hibernate in winter. Other behaviors are unique to an individual creature such as the way your dog barks twice when he wants to be let outside. Many behaviors are unique to a particular being on a particular occasion, such as the way you react when you find a twenty-dollar bill on the street at the end of a bad day.

Forms of behavior

Actions are one subset of behavior, and states of mind — emotions and moods — are another. This is not obvious. A person can be angry without necessarily doing anything physical like hitting or shouting. Nonetheless, the anger that is felt is a response to stimuli. Perhaps an expensive bill has arrived in the mail or your late-adolescence hormones are surging.

Mental illness falls into the category of behavior though this may not seem obvious, either. Depression does not seem to be a person's response to the world but rather an emotional state that descends upon him or her. In the same way, there is no single event or series of events that explain why a person develops schizophrenia.

However, scientists believe mental illness emerges in response to a series of causative events inside and outside the body. These events may be subtle, they may not be linked in time, and many of them remain unknown, but they are sus-

pected to have some influence on when and whether mood disorders appear. Thus, mood disorders fall into the category of behavior.

In another not-so-obvious connection, personality is behavior. This makes sense when you consider that personality is the sum total of a person's physical, mental, emotional, and social characteristics that distinguish that person from everyone else. Consistent patterns of behavior lead us to describe individuals as being docile and sweet or brusque and standoffish. And yet the typically quiet person might sometimes be quite vocal and the typically aloof individual might sometimes be quite sociable, because behavior always depends on a context.

Since mood and personality fall into the category of behavior, it stands to

Behavior includes not only actions but also the emotions we feel such as anxiety or joy.

reason that thinking itself is a behavior. So when you do addition in your head or try to puzzle out a dream from the night before, you are behaving. The type of thinking behavior that involves knowing and perceiving is called intelligence or cognition. Speed of thought, problem-solving skills, and the ability to make connections are different aspects of this behavior.

Behavioral genetics

Researchers in the field of behavioral genetics study variation in behavior as it is affected by genes, which are the units of heredity passed down from parents to offspring. A fuller description of these genes is provided in Chapter 2.

Scientists realize that genes by themselves do not control behavior. Genes enable organisms to respond to and use what is around them in their environments. At the same time, environments influence the actions of genes.

Unfortunately, the term "environment" often leads to confusion because it has a different meaning in behavioral genetics than the one that ordinarily comes to mind. As an ecological term, environment means the physical world. As a genetic term, environment means all influences other than inherited factors. Here's a short list of some typical envi-

As any parent knows too well, biologically related children can differ widely in behavior.

ronmental factors that to one degree or another affect behavior: family and friends, home and workplace, and specific experiences from everyday life. These are aspects of our external, social world. Other environmental factors belong to the internal, biological world: nutrients, hormones, viruses, bacteria, toxins, and other products that affect the body during prenatal development and throughout life. Environments are addressed at greater length in Chapter 3.

People working in the field of behavioral genetics agree that genes and environments are both essential and interdependent factors in behavior. Their field is called behavioral *genetics*, not because they think genes are more important than environments but because they use gene-based research tools to sort out the factors that contribute to the variation in behavior. These tools are described in Chapter 4.

Behavioral genetic researchers study all sorts of life forms, simple and complex, from worms and fruit flies to chimpanzees and humans. Their work overlaps and complements behavioral research happening in other fields such as biology, psychology, physiology, medical genetics, evolutionary science, and neuroscience, to name a few. The particular interest of behavioral geneticists is in what makes members of a species (especially the human species) *differ* in their behavior. The field also is defined by a particular focus on topics that have

substantial social significance. Three such topics — mood disorders, impulsivity, and intelligence — are treated in Chapters 5, 6, and 7.

Margaret's ambition

What accounts for the fact that some people are more accomplished athletically than others? This is a question that interests many scientists including behavioral genetic researchers. It also is one that would interest Margaret, the woman who plans to groom her daughter into a professional golfer like Tiger Woods.

Tiger is an intriguing case study because his athletic performance is so extraordinary. He was a precocious child who before his third birthday could beat far older players on the course. By age 15, he had won five junior world tournaments. Then he claimed three U.S. amateur championships in a row. He turned professional at age 20 and earned $800,000 in prize money his first season.

At age 21, he became the youngest winner of the Masters Tournament, and within four years he had his career grand slam — a victory in each of golf's four major tournaments. With a growing collection of victories, he is surpassing the records set by Jack Nicklaus and other legends of the sport.

Tiger combines a powerful swing with great putting skills, excellent stamina, incredible discipline, and impressive self-control. He has all the assets for an

Genes and environments are interdependent: one does not have an effect on behavior without the other.

Success in any endeavor requires more than an advantageous set of genes.

exceptional career. His success is so unusual that it compels us to ask, where does Tiger get it? Or, as Margaret might put it, "How can I get some of that for my child?"

We do not know whether Tiger was born with a set of genes that are particularly advantageous for golf (molecular study could someday shed light on this), though we might intuitively conclude that he is built for the sport. We do know that at an early age his father Earl Woods recognized, nurtured, shaped, and pushed his son's talent. We also know that Tiger was willing and eager to be coached, to work extremely hard, and to aim for high goals.

We can assume that chance has played a part in Tiger's success. Just consider how he might have turned out if his father had not liked golf, if he had developed a debilitating illness as a youth, or if he had been born a few decades earlier when most golf courses were Whites-only.

Genes, environment, choice, and chance: each plays off the others over the course of a lifetime. Biographers have already begun to speculate on how these various threads have woven together to make Tiger who he is. But for Margaret proactively to *make* Cassandra into a successful professional golfer, she has to control all the variables — and that is simply not possible.

Science in society

As a field, behavioral genetics is concerned not so much with individuals such as Tiger or Cassandra, but with patterns of variety among groups of people. It is concerned with questions of probability; for example, what is the probability that you will have good hand-eye coordination given a particular set of genes and a particular set of environmental conditions?

Behavioral genetics does not have an answer to the question just posed, though it might someday. And it is not the domain of behavioral genetics to answer the question of whether Margaret *ought* to aggressively manipulate her daughter's future. It is society through its values, cultural practices, and laws that determines how we should behave. Behavioral genetics can only help us understand what makes us behave as we do.

Individual scientists who study behavior cannot and should not decide which behaviors are valued and acceptable and which are outside the norm. Such important decisions must be made by society as a whole.

RESOURCES FOR CHAPTER 1

Biological Sciences Curriculum Study (BSCS). 2000. *Genes, environment, and human behavior.* Colorado Springs: BSCS.

Carey, G. 2003. *Human genetics for the social sciences.* Thousand Oaks, CA: Sage Publications.

Dick, D. M. and R. J. Rose. 2002. "Behavior genetics: What's new? What's next?" *Current Directions in Psychological Science 11*, no. 2: 70-74.

Plomin, R., J. C. DeFries, G. E. McClearn, and M. Rutter. 1997. *Behavioral genetics,* 3rd ed. New York: Freeman Press.

Shapiro, L. 2002. "Woods successfully defends title, captures third overall." *Washington Post,* 15 April, C-1.

"Tiger Woods." 2001. (Accessed 3 October); available from http://www.infoplease.com/ipsa/A0109760.html.

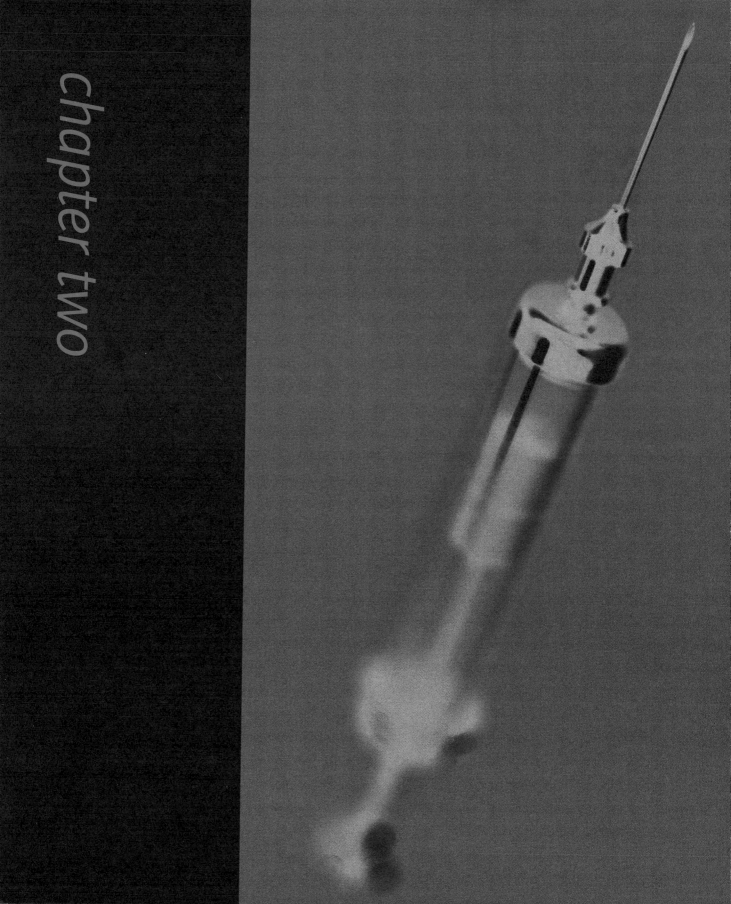

chapter two

HOW DO GENES WORK WITHIN THEIR ENVIRONMENTS?

■ ■ ■ Hoda, a perplexed nurse

Hoda has been a pediatric nurse for twenty years, and today was one of her tougher days. It's August and so a good number of the young patients had come in for school immunizations. Hoda thinks to herself on the way home that if she could have a nickel for every child who cries at getting a shot, she could retire a rich woman.

Her glum perspective eases up a bit as she gets further away from the clinic. It was really hot in there today, she tells herself, and for a lot of the children it is a strange place. She considers the fact that almost every child who gets upset by a shot is easily consoled with a simple sticker. And while some children are born crybabies, many others never put up a fuss at vaccination.

Hoda used to think that a child's attitude towards shots depended on the parent with him or her at the clinic, but since she became a parent herself she is not so sure about that. Her older son has never minded shots, but her younger son is a big baby.

Hoda knows that her own conduct as nurse has considerable influence on how her young patients behave. She tries to be gentle and to do her business as quickly as she can. While that works for most children, it is not enough for others. And then there's always the child who is no trouble for one vaccination, but who makes a big fuss for the next. "Kids!" thinks Hoda. "Will I ever figure them out?"

The human genome

The complete set of genetic material for any organism is called its genome. In recent decades, information about the genomes of several organisms has been pouring out of a massive international effort called the Human Genome Project. This "sea of data," as it has been called, confirms the view that genes operate within really big and complex systems.

The human genome is organized into two sets of twenty-three chromosomes, forty-six in all. These chromosomes are made of a chemical substance called DNA (deoxyribonucleic acid), and this DNA, in turn, is made of smaller units: nitrogen-containing molecules called nucleotides or bases. There are four different bases, called adenine (A), cytosine (C), thymine (T), and guanine (G). The bases are paired and linked together to form a double-stranded helix. The order of bases strung along chromosomal DNA is critical, as we will explain in a moment.

The human genome contains three billion pairs of these bases. Measured with a yardstick, this makes six feet of DNA — not so very long, except that all of it fits, coiled up, inside the nucleus of a single cell. Indeed, the entire genome in identical form is packed into nearly every nucleus of the body's one hundred trillion cells.

The human genome is quite large, but it is not all that large compared to the genomes of other life forms. A tiny germ called *mycoplasma genitalium* has one of the smallest genomes yet contains more than 580,000 base pairs. Wheat has ten times more DNA than humans.

Function of the human genome

Size is not the only dimension that makes the human genome impressive. Functional operation is another. At seemingly random spots along a chromosome's strand of DNA, base pairs are organized into units that operate together. These are the genes.

There is an important term for those "seemingly random spots along a chro-

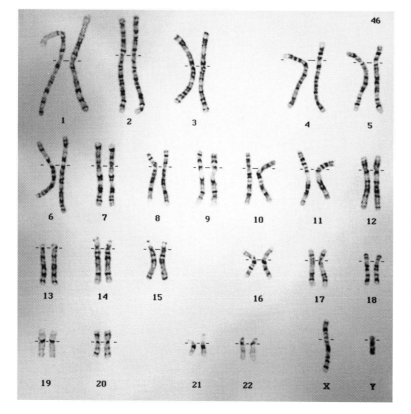

mosome's strand of DNA," and it will appear frequently in this text. That term is locus; the plural is loci. It means "location of the gene on the chromosome." The word locus also has come to stand for "the location of a segment of DNA within a gene."

Each gene varies in the order of the bases along its length. The average human gene is three thousand base pairs long. The human genome contains an estimated 30,000 or more genes, yet these genes comprise less than 5 percent of the genomic material.

Put simply, this is what genes do: They provide the template for a series of intricate steps that cells follow to create proteins. A gene's string of bases is organized into triplets. The sequence of DNA triplets that defines a gene is copied into a string of RNA (ribonucleic acid, a chemical similar and complementary to DNA) triplets. In most cases, each RNA triplet codes for one of twenty different small molecules called amino acids (fondly referred to by science teachers as "the building blocks of the body"). Most of the amino acids have names ending in "ine" such as alanine, glycine, and isoleucine. The amino acids coded for by a gene link together into a polypeptide chain. These chains can be hundreds or thousands of links long (shorter strands are referred to simply as "peptide chains"). A protein is formed when (in most cases) two or more chains link together into a three-dimensional structure.

Proteins make up the structure of cells: hair, cartilage, bone, and the other physical components of the body are built from protein. In the form of hormones, enzymes, and antibodies, proteins direct cell activity. Proteins help transport materials between cells and they help cells communicate with each other.

Another critical task of proteins exemplifies that old phrase "turnabout is fair play." Proteins are constructed through gene activity and — in the form of hormones, growth factors, and other regulatory molecules — proteins also *affect* gene activity.

The adjective that describes this phenomenon is epigenetic. *Epi* is a Greek root meaning "upon," and epigenesis means the process of affecting the action of a gene without altering the DNA of the gene itself. Epigenetic effects are produced not only by proteins but also by RNA; by certain genes with managerial responsibilities; and by the imprinting of genes (a little-understood phenomenon by which a gene expresses itself differently depending upon whether it was inherited from the mother or the father).

These epigenetic factors are what cause some cells to turn into skin while others become part of the liver, bone, or brain, even though all the cells contain the same package of DNA. Epigenetic mechanisms remain important throughout life, selectively triggering the genes in various tissues in response to environmental stimuli.

A protein can be visualized as a long strand of material that bends and folds into a complex three-dimensional shape. This long strand typically is created from two or more chains of amino acids (and sometimes other chemicals) that have linked together. Each separate chain is created according to the instructions contained in a gene.

This brings us back to what happens when genes are triggered: in scientific shorthand, this is described as "genes regulating proteins" or "genes coding for proteins." (To be technically accurate, some genes "code" for RNA and some genes do not actually "code for" anything, but rather serve as a catalyst.) In common jargon, genes also "go into play" or "express themselves" or, more technically, "undergo transcription and translation." In a nutshell, here's what these terms all mean. The body obtains protein from food and digests it, breaking it down into the twenty different amino acids. Amino acids are stored inside cells. Prompted into action by epigenetic factors that have themselves been prompted by environmental influences, the genes inside a cell issue the instructions for reassembling amino acids into polypeptide chains that combine to form new proteins that are then available to perform a variety of tasks in the body.

Genes have one more important function. They are the mechanism by which the template for making proteins is passed down from one generation to the next. Sperm cells and egg cells each carry a half complement of chromosomes, and at conception the two half-sets combine to produce a new organism with a unique combination of genes.

As was just mentioned, somewhere around 30,000 genes are contained in the human genome. Yet the body produces far more than 30,000 proteins. This is possible because the amino acids produced by genes can combine in different ways to make different proteins.

Nearly all the cells of the body contain the entire set of genes. But within each cell no more than about 5 percent of the genes are ever expressed. The genes in the cells of one tissue (for example, kidney cells) may — under certain environmental conditions — become activated and express themselves while the equivalent genes in the cells of another tissue (for example, the brain) remain inactive.

The bottom line is that the 30,000-some human genes are capable of producing a many-times-larger number of proteins. These proteins work independently and in combinations to create an even larger number of outcomes in the cells of the body.

Variety within the human genome

In addition to size and function, the genome is impressive along another dimension, and that is variety. For each species, the genome comes in unlimited versions — it differs in every individual within a species. This difference is small percentage-wise, but it has profound effects.

The genetic sequence of any human is estimated to be 99.9 percent identical to that of any other human's. Expressed as a percent that is an overwhelming similarity. However, one tenth of a percent of three billion base pairs of DNA is 3 million, a very large number.

Some of those tenth-of-a-percent differences occur in the genes. Every human has the same basic package of genes, but each gene may show up in a different version, called an allele. A gene's alleles differ slightly from one another in terms of the order that the four bases — A, T, C, and G — appear along the DNA strand. Scientists believe that there are two or more variants for most human genes; the average number of normal alleles for a gene is estimated at 14, but some genes have 50 or more. Humans are diploid, which means they carry two alleles for every gene (one inherited from the father and one from the mother); the two alleles in a given pair may be identical (in which case they are homozygous) or different (heterozygous). Each person is unique in

Nitrogen-containing molecules called nucleotides or bases are paired and lined up on a twisting ladder-like structure (a double helix) to form a chromosome. Sections of these base pairs operate together as genes. Other sections have other functions. Species differ in their number of chromosomes.

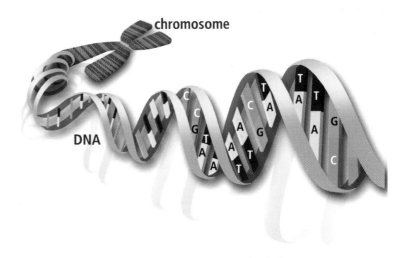
chromosome

DNA

terms of his or her particular combination of alleles.

An individual's unique set of alleles is referred to as his or her genotype. (The word "genotype" is also used to refer to a subset of genes, a small part of the whole genome, that is relevant to the particular trait being studied.) Through the actions of the proteins it directs, each genotype contributes to a unique set of observable human traits, or phenotype.

In some cases, alleles behave in an additive fashion: each allele contributes to the variation in a phenotype in a separate, measurable way. One way to think of additive genetic variance is with the metaphor of a potluck meal. Each person brings a dish; the degree to which the meal is a culinary success depends on the tastiness of individual appetizers, casseroles, and desserts.

In other cases, alleles are nonadditive. A nonadditive effect occurs when an individual's two alleles for a gene are dissimilar and one has dominance over the other so its genotype more heavily influences the phenotype. Nonadditive effects also occur when there is epistasis: one allele at one location in the genome affects the expression of another allele at another location. Thus additive and nonadditive effects characterize the relationship not only between the two alleles for one gene (in scientific speak we could say "the two alleles at one locus"), but also between alleles of different genes ("alleles at different loci").

Similarity across genomes

There is yet another admirable feature of the genome, and this is its consistency across species. Just as with individual genomes within a species, genomes across species differ less than you might expect. About half of all fruit fly genes have parallel genes in the human, while the mouse genome corresponds to the human almost completely.

The gene sequences of human and chimpanzee are 99.4 percent alike. What differs between the two species are a very few genes (not just alleles, which are variations of the same gene) and, more importantly, the activity levels of the genes. For example, certain genes that affect human brain function are much more active in humans compared to the corresponding genes in the chimpanzee. This is enough to account for the major differences in appearances and behaviors between human and chimp.

There is an interesting explanation for why the genomes of different species have so much in common. Scientists propose that all species stem from a single, simple organism that existed eons ago. Later species grew out of that original species like branches from the trunk of a tree. In every new species, some of the DNA of its predecessors is conserved.

This process of change is known as evolution, and the mechanisms by which species emerge include mutation, natural selection, and genetic drift. A mutation is a change in the DNA of a gene that alters

Genes are "conserved" across species, which means humans are extremely similar genetically to chimpanzees. Shared genes differ in their activity level, and this accounts for much of the difference between the two species.

the genetic message coded by that gene. Mutations can occur in any part of a gene inside any cell at any point in life. They can be triggered for example by radiation, malnutrition, aging, and physical trauma to the cell.

Cells in most parts of the body frequently make copies of themselves so that tissues can grow and old cells can be replaced, and this is when most mutations occur. In this copying process, billions of bases are copied, and with every copy there are a few errors. One or more bases are put in the wrong place, left out, or changed. Sometimes extra copies are made of a string of bases or of whole chromosomes. Sometimes a gene moves to a new location or is deleted.

Errors occur about every million cell replications, perhaps more frequently. In most cases, these mutation have little or no effect on a gene's action. But in rare cases, the mutation has a major effect; the amino acids produced from a gene containing an error are different or do not appear. This genotypic difference may sometimes lead to a phenotypic difference that affects, for good or bad, the organism's ability to thrive or survive.

If the mutation occurs in a gamete of an individual (the egg or sperm cell involved in reproduction), then the new mutation appears in the cells of that individual's offspring. Such mutations lead to variety within a species. If the mutation offers an advantage for survival, then individuals with the mutation will leave more

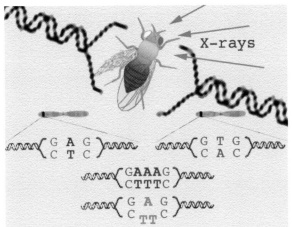

descendents in the next generation: this is part of natural selection. Over many generations the mutation may become predominant in the species, and over a great many generations, a collection of advantageous mutations in an isolated population can lead to the development of a new species.

The third evolutionary mechanism mentioned above, genetic drift, occurs when members of a species are separated into distinct populations; for example, if one group of humans migrates a long distance away from another group. Within each population, certain alleles are passed onto the next generation by chance, increasing or decreasing their likelihood of being passed on again to the third generation. Over time, the number of alleles that remain in the population are reduced. The smaller the population, the greater the reductions in allelic variety over time. The separated populations diverge—drift apart—in terms of the alleles they carry.

A change to the DNA, called a mutation, can be triggered by any of a number of causes. Most mutations result from simple errors introduced during replication of the cell. However, some result from physical damage to the cell. In this illustration, an insect is exposed to radiation, possibly leading to one or more mutations, such as the transposition of a base pair; the insertion of extra base pairs; or the duplication of one extra base in a pair. Such mutations sometimes alter the actions of a gene.

Imagining the genome

To summarize, the genome has an extremely large number of component parts yet is infinitesimal in size. It appears nearly identically in billions of cells, but operates dissimilarly inside different cells. One species' genome translates into an incredibly broad range of genotypes and a far broader range of phenotypes. At the same time, genomes across species resemble each other remarkably.

The genome is so curious that we use metaphors to help us get a handle on it. It has been described as a codebook, a book of life, or an encyclopedia. It has been likened to an instruction book, with each gene being one instruction in this book.

But these metaphors are not holding up under the weight of our expanding knowledge. Today, scientists realize that the genome is much more dynamic than any kind of book. They know the same genes in the cells of different tissues may lead to different effects in different parts of the body (this is called pleiotropy) and that, by the same token, the same effects can result from different genes or sets of genes (this is called genetic heterogeneity). And scientists know that which instructions genes issue, and whether or not they do, depends entirely on the environmental context at any given moment in time.

Furthermore, they have learned that the genome contains many other important elements besides instruction-giving genes. Mixed among and within the coding genes, which occupy just a small fraction of the total DNA, are non-coding sequences and other features that have been given names based on what is known about their structure or function: promoters, enhancers, pseudogenes, tandem repeats, telomeres, centromeres, and the like. Some of these elements play critical epigenetic roles, managing the genes that do code for protein expression. Others have minor roles or no

discernable role — we might more wisely say that their role still awaits discovery.

So a new metaphor is replacing the metaphor of genome-as-text. This is the metaphor of the genome as a community or collective, working together for a shared purpose. Just as a cast, crew, directors, and producers work together to put on a play, so the elements of the genome work with each other, and with epigenetic characters, to express the chemical products required by a body in the process of life.

Behavior and the genome

All of this description about the genome is simply background to the question at hand, which is how genes, operating within environments, connect to behavior. Behavior results from the genetic coding that occurs in cells throughout the body, but especially in the nervous system: the brain, spine, and network of nerves through which information is communicated throughout the body, electrically and chemically. Put simply, behavior results from lots and lots of ongoing activity by many, many genes pressed into action by the environment and through epigenetic factors.

Blood types, some simple metabolic processes, and a few physical traits stem from the actions of a single gene, irrespective of environment. Some health disorders such as cystic fibrosis, early-onset Alzheimer's, and Huntington's

disease have been tracked to one gene. Most physical traits and conditions — such as height, blood pressure, weight, and digestive activity — stem from many genes that vary in activity depending on environmental contexts. The same is true for all complex behaviors. Each is affected by multiple genes interacting with multiple environmental influences. For any given behavior, relevant genes and environmental factors number in the dozens, hundreds, or perhaps thousands.

Unfortunately, many people have a different impression. They think that a gene controls a behavioral trait, period. This is genetic determinism, that is, the belief that the development of an organism is determined solely by genetic factors. Genetic determinism is a false belief. It comes from misunderstandings of scientific research.

A great many studies have explored possible connections between genetic factors and specific behaviors, such as the age at which a young person begins to smoke and drink, the friends one selects, a person's tendency toward divorce, grooming habits, and one's willingness to take risks, to name just a few. Some of these studies have found that close relatives tend to be more alike for the trait in question than people who are not as closely related. But these kinds of studies only identify correlations between people with similar genetic profiles and certain behaviors. Correlations are related rates of incidence, reflecting how much and in

Scientists have only begun to explore the complex relationship between genetics, environments, and human habits, tendencies, and addictions.

Correlation does not mean causation: ice cream sales and crime both rise with the outside temperature, but one does not cause the other. In the same way, a person may have certain alleles for a gene and behave a certain way, but that does not mean the allele causes the behavior.

what way two elements co-occur.

It's important to realize that correlation is *not* causation: ice cream consumption and crime both go up in the summer (a positive correlation), but one does not necessarily cause the other. Correlation studies in behavioral genetics do not reveal anything about the specific underlying genes and they only offer clues as to the relevant environmental variables.

Sometimes researchers will identify a particular allele for a gene that is found in some people who have the trait and that therefore is speculated to potentially have something to do with the trait. One cannot jump to a conclusion from this kind of correlation study, because additional genes and various environmental factors also are potentially involved.

So while behavioral genetic studies do not provide any justification for simplistic talk about "a gene for starting to smoke" or "a gene for divorce," people sometimes talk like that anyway. There are many explanations for why people make these kinds of false statements. Sometimes a scientist overstates the significance of his or her study, sometimes a reporter misinterprets research, sometimes the headline to an article oversimplifies the story, and sometimes naive members of the public jump to the wrong conclusion. Such errors are not mutually exclusive. But the fact is that so far, scientific research has not confirmed any one-to-one correspondence between a gene and a human behavior. Behavior results from the activity of multiple genes amidst the influence of multiple environmental factors.

Hoda's perplexity

We know that there is no "gene for taking shots bravely." In a way that's too bad, because if there were it would explain what Hoda in her career as a pediatric nurse has observed — that some children are simply afraid of shots and others are not. But a single gene hypothesis could not explain what Hoda has further observed — that children's responses to the needle vary continuously across a wide spectrum and that an individual child's responses can be inconsistent.

Hoda might be interested in hearing about a classic animal behavior study conducted several decades ago. In this experiment, scientists took a group of ordinary field mice and put them, one at a time, into a brightly lit open box. The mice had never been in the box before, and they reacted with a range of behaviors.

Some appeared to be fearful. They huddled motionless along the sides. Others appeared to be more brave. They roamed about, though they did not stray far from the sides. A few mice wandered freely, even venturing into the middle.

Using various tools, the scientists precisely measured each mouse's movements. They selected the most immobilized and the most active. Then they bred these selected mice, fearful with fearful and brave with brave.

When the next generation came along, scientists again tested each mouse in the box. They selected the most timid offspring of the timid parents and the bravest offspring of the brave parents. The selected offspring were again bred, like with like. The scientists kept up such inbreeding for thirty generations.

With each generation, the mice in the timid group became, as a whole, more timid, while the mice in the brave group became, as a whole, more brave. The two lines of mice came from the same original stock, and they were kept and raised under identical conditions. But their responses to the box were becoming progressively more different.

To make sure no uncontrolled factor was affecting the behavior of the mice, the scientists moved the experiment up a notch. They had mice born to the timid line foster-mothered by a mouse from the brave line, and vice versa. They also mixed young from each line into one litter to be raised together by one female adult.

Nothing changed. Mice from the line inbred for timidity showed fear when placed in the open box. Mice from the line inbred for bravery responded with courage.[1]

Scientists point to these experiments as proof that behavior traits can be influenced by heredity. These experiments also proved something else: that more than one inherited factor was at work to affect mice behavior. We know this because the intensity of bravery and fearfulness in the respective lines of mice occurred over many generations and continued to evolve. If only one or two genes had been involved, the extreme form of the behavior would have been universal within a few generations (because each parent only passes down one allele for

Many genes, plus many environmental factors, shape the behavior of a mouse placed inside an open box.

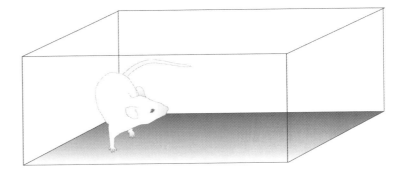

Holding, prodding, and petting a rabbit can make it bolder, but that sort of shaped behavior is not transmitted from one generation to the next.

any gene from the two that it has itself).

Fearfulness, its opposite bravery, and other behaviors are called quantitative genetic traits because the phenotypes (the observable behaviors) associated with the underlying genotypes vary by measurable quantities or degrees. The original generation of mice included those that were not very fearful, moderately fearful, and quite fearful, plus others in between. If scored on a scale and plotted on a graph, the range in behavior would look like a bell-shaped curve. This kind of trait is also called continuous since its particular characteristics vary continuously from one extreme to the other. [The opposite kind of trait is discontinuous — you either have it or you do not, such as a sixth finger on your hands. Being able to roll your tongue is an example of a discontinuous behavioral trait, but it is the exception rather than the rule. Almost all behavioral traits are continuous.]

Each gene involved in a quantitative trait is called a quantitative trait locus (QTL). The term QTL is the technical way of saying "one location among many in the genome that affects a continuous trait." Each QTL may have a major effect or a minor effect, but it does not have an exclusive effect.

In addition, as was emphasized before, there is also the effects of the environment. As an experienced nurse, Hoda believes that how she behaves has some moderating effect on her young patients.

Scientific support for her belief has been nicely provided by another animal experiment, this time involving rabbits. When placed in an open box, rabbits — like the mice — show a range of responses from withdrawal to quick acclimation. But researchers have learned that rabbit reactions can be molded by the amount of stimulation they receive while very young. Baby rabbits that are handled by humans and exposed to minor shocks or temperature changes are more likely to be more free-ranging in the box later compared to a control group of bunnies.

The degree of fearlessness in rabbits correlates directly with the amount of stimulation they receive early in life. But because the rabbit reactions are shaped by external stimuli, fearlessness as a trait does not pass from one generation to the next. Rabbits that have been stimulated do not produce offspring that are more fearless, as a group, than offspring of unstimulated rabbits.[2]

Some caveats

The mice and rabbit studies just described take us only so far. They show us that genes and environment both have effects on behaviors, but they do not tell us how they work together to do so.

Furthermore, these are *animal* studies. We can put mice and rabbits into boxes and fancifully label their behavior "brave" or "fearful," but we cannot extrapolate from that to how humans

might behave in strange situations.

We cannot take human adults, test them on a particular task and then, based on performance, select some to breed together in order to concentrate certain inherited factors in their children. Likewise, we cannot deliberately experiment with human babies by handling them differently to see how their behavior might be affected as they mature.

But we can give these animal studies credit for helping us understand the essential point that both inherited and environmental factors contribute to behavior. Hoda, in her years of working with children, intuitively knows this. She is aware that children tend toward certain temperaments, but that her own actions, as well as other factors beyond anyone's control, affect the behavior patients manifest when in her clinic. Hoda probably understands children better than she realizes.

Scientists believe that each person's package of genes might partially explain tendencies, such as why one child has an outgoing personality and another is more shy. Yet many non-genetic factors also affect how a human acts in a particular circumstance.

Notes

1   See Clark, W. and M. Grunstein (2000, pgs. 86–88) and in Plomin *et al.* (1997, pgs. 62–66) for discussions of the mice studies. The research discussed is DeFries *et al.* (1978).

2   See Clark, W. and M. Grunstein (2000, pgs. 90–92) for a discussion of the rabbit studies.

RESOURCES FOR CHAPTER 2

Avise, J. C. 2001. "Evolving genomic metaphors: A new look at the language of the DNA." *Science* 294: 86-87.

Biological Sciences Curriculum Study (BSCS). 2000. *Genes, environment, and human behavior.* Colorado Springs: BSCS.

Butler, D. 2000. "Celera in talks to launch private sector human proteome project." *Nature* 403: 815-816.

Carollo, V. 2003. "Grain genes and beyond: bioinformatics tools for the wheat genome project." (Accessed 9 June); available at http://www.wheatimprovement.org/Forum/5/Carollo.html.

Carey, G. 2003. *Human genetics for the social sciences.* Thousand Oaks, CA: Sage Publications.

Clark, W. and M. Grunstein. 2000. *Are we hardwired? The role of genes in human behavior.* New York: Oxford University Press.

"DNA Structural Analysis Sequenced Genome." 2003. (Accessed 10 June); available at www.cbs.dtu.dk/services/GenomeAtlas/Bacteria/Mycoplasma/genitalium/G37/.

Da Silva, W. 2003. 15 September 2003. "Rip up life's blueprint: It's time to rethink the way we look at the human genome." *New Scientist.* 12.

DeFries, J. et al. 1978. "Response to 30 generations of selection for open-field activity in laboratory mice." *Behavior Genetics* 8: 3-13.

Dean H. Hamer, Ph. D. 2003. (home page, accessed 31 January); available at http://rex.nci.nih.gov/RESEARCH/basic/biochem/hamer.htm

"Destined to divorce." 14 July 2001. *New Scientist.* 15.

Enard, W., P. Khaitovich, J. Klose, S. Zöllner, F. Heissing, P. Giavalisco, K. Nieselt-Struwe, E. Muchmore, A. Varki, R. Ravid, G. M. Doxiadis, R. E. Bontrop, S. Paabo. 2002. "Intra-and interspecific variation in primate expression patterns. *Science* 296: 340-343.

Fraser, C.M., J. D.Gocayne, O. White, M. D. Adams, R. A. Clayton, R. D. Fleischmann, C. J. Bult, A. R. Kerlavage, G. Sutton, J. M. Kelley. 1995. "The minimal gene complement of mycoplasma genitalium." *Science* 270: 397-403.

Gottesman, I. I. 2001. "Psychopathology through a life span — genetic prism." *American Psychologist* 56: 864-878.

Hemp. J. 24 May 2003. "People and chimps belong together on the family tree." *New Scientist.* 15.

Howard Hughes Medical Institute. 2003. "The genes we share." (accessed 6 June); available at http://www.hhmi.org/genesweshare/e300.html.

Patterson, M. 2002. "A question of grooming." *Nature Reviews Genetics* 3: 89.

Pennisi, E. 2001. "Behind the scenes of gene expression." *Science* 293: 1064-1067.

Pennisi, E. 2002. "Gene activity clocks brain's fast evolution." *Science* 296: 233-235.

Plomin, R., J. C. DeFries, G. E. McClearn, and M. Rutter. 1997. *Behavioral genetics*, 3rd ed. New York: Freeman Press.

Rutter, M. 2002. "Nature, nurture, and development: From evangelism through science toward policy and practice." *Child Development* 73: 1-21.

U.S. Department of Energy Human Genome Program. 2003. "Genomics and its impact on science and society: Beyond the human genome project." (Accessed 9 June); available at http://www.ornl.gov/TechResources/Human_Genome/publicat/primer2001/.

Weiss, R. 2000. "For DNA, a defining moment." *Washington Post.* 23 May, A-1 and A-17-18.

Wu, C.-t. and J. R. Morris. 2001. "Genes, genetics, and epigenetics: A correspondence." *Science* 293: 1103-1105.

chapter three

HOW DO ENVIRONMENTS IMPINGE UPON GENES?

3

■ ■ ■ Skip, a regretful man

When Skip was a boy he often pestered his mother with questions. "Why can't I have my own room?" he would ask. "Why can't I have a bike? Why do we have to eat casserole every night?" But his mother would only reply with aphorisms he didn't understand. "If pigs had wings they would fly," she would say. Or sometimes she would say, "If wishes were candy it would be Christmas every day."

Those annoying sayings echo in his ears tonight. He surely wishes he could make like a pig and fly out of the stinking mess of his life. It's not his fault, Skip thinks bitterly. He had to drop out of high school to earn money for the family. But then he thinks how he didn't have to get his girl-friend pregnant. Twice. And he could have gone back to school or learned a trade. He just never seemed to have the time, energy, or cash.

So here he is at thirty-two, divorced and alone, and no further ahead than when he was eighteen. He's just an assistant manager at an all-night diner with no one to talk to but tired-out waitresses, surly cooks, and grumpy customers. It didn't have to be this way, he muses despondently. Hadn't he been a real charmer, a really handsome kid? Wasn't he the best hitter on his Little League team? Didn't he used to dream of becoming an astronaut?

Skip thinks about Marlon Brando's wailing complaint in the classic movie, *On the Waterfront*. "I could'a been a contender!" Me too, thinks Skip. "I really could have been somebody. So why have I turned out to be such a loser?"

Environment illustrated

Three examples will illustrate how environments impinge upon genes. They concern a plant, a human disease, and a human behavior.

In a classic experiment, seven genetically distinct yarrow plants were collected and three cuttings taken from each plant. One cutting of each genotype was planted at low, medium, and high elevations, respectively.

When the plants matured, no one genotype grew best at all altitudes, and at each altitude the seven genotypes fared differently. For example, one genotype grew the tallest at the medium elevation but attained only middling height at the other two elevations. The best growers at low and high elevation grew poorly at medium elevation. The medium altitude produced the worst overall results, but still yielded one tall and two medium-tall samples. Altitude had an effect on each genotype, but not to the same degree nor in the same way.[1]

The second example illustrating environmental effects involves the human disease called PKU. This is the common name for a medical disorder, phenylketonuria, which results when the body does not produce enough of a particular liver enzyme. In the absence of this enzyme, an amino acid known as phenylalanine does not get converted into the next amino acid in a biochemical pathway, and therefore too much phenylalanine passes into the blood and other tissues. This disturbs brain development, leading to mental retardation and other problems.

PKU affects approximately 1 out of every 15,000 infants in the U.S. However, most affected infants do not grow up impaired because of a standard screening program used in the U.S. and other industrialized societies. Newborns found to have high levels of phenylalanine in their blood can be put on a special, phenylalanine-free diet. If they are put on this diet right away and stay on it, these children avoid the severe effects of PKU.

PKU is a genetic condition that stems from any of a number of different mutations in a gene that codes for amino acids

Some medical disorders are caused by faulty instructions from a single gene. PKU is such a disorder. If babies with this disorder are identified at birth, treatment can prevent the tragic health consequences of PKU.

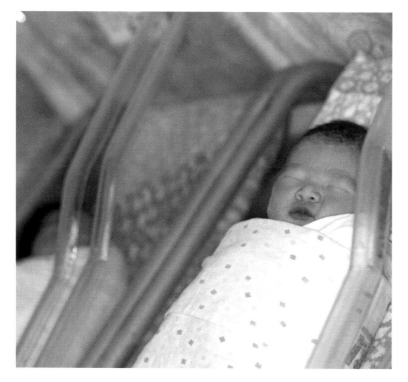

that combine to form an enzyme that converts phenylalanine. (Scientists often refer to alleles that lead to disorders as mutations, though all alleles — both those with positive and negative effects —emerge at some point in the evolutionary history of a species through the process of mutation. In this text, we will refer to such mutations as "disease-related alleles" or "problematic alleles.")

Researchers know that other so-called modifier genes also play a role in PKU — these are genes that affect another gene, thereby altering the latter gene's effect on the phenotype. Thus, there are many different genotypes underlying PKU, and this certainly is one reason why the disease manifests itself differently in each child.

Environment is another reason. The form and severity of PKU are profoundly influenced by such factors as when the condition is diagnosed, how soon the special diet is imposed, and how strictly it is followed.

Yet in an interesting twist, environmental effects decline over time. A child who does not receive a modified diet within days of birth is at great risk for brain damage. The same child in adolescence can follow a slightly more flexible diet without ill effect. Some adults with PKU have binged occasionally or moved off the diet altogether without observable losses in cognitive function (though standard medical advice is to maintain the diet for life).

The third example for environmental effects concerns human intelligence. Scientists theorize that many different aspects of brain function factor into our ability to reason and to learn, such as energy metabolism and neuronal transmission speed. To the extent that genes trigger the protein activity that constructs the brain and are essential to its function, they play a role in intelligence.

Tests used to measure individual intelligence are called IQ tests (for intelligence quotient). Performance on these tests varies widely among individuals: most tested individuals obtain scores that fall into a middle range, while a minority obtain scores that fall farther out on the high and low ends. All the scores plotted out form a sort of bell-shaped curve.

In 1987, a scientist named James Flynn reported that, based on IQ data from many countries, the raw test scores have been rising rapidly for several decades. So while the bell-shaped varia-

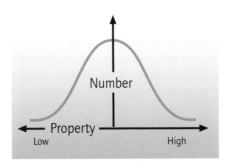

The Bell Shaped Curve

In a randomly selected group of people, behavior traits tend to vary along a continuum known as a bell shaped curve. In this illustration, a trait is indicated as a "property" that can range from low to high. An example would be scores on an intelligence test: most people tend to score near the middle, but some score lower or higher. The higher or lower the score, the fewer the number of people achieving those scores.

better functioning on some tasks measured by IQ tests. Recall once again that genes code for amino acids, the building blocks of the proteins that create the physical structures of cells and trigger activity inside them. Therefore, while the environment may be altering brain development and causing IQ to rise, it is doing so through the mechanism of the genes.

IQ scores are rising, but this does not necessarily mean that today's children are smarter than their parents. There are many theories that explain the IQ rise, but they all come down to the same basic idea: human environments are interacting with human genes to produce different results than before.

tion remains, performance across the board has gone up.

This phenomenon has been dubbed the Flynn effect. Flynn's research suggests that a good deal of this IQ gain can be attributed to improved performance on analytical and visual/spatial problems. Performance on verbal and mathematical problems has increased, but not as rapidly.

The overall rise in IQ scores cannot possibly be due to new genetic mutations introduced and dispersed throughout the world's population, since that kind of evolutionary change would take many hundreds or thousands of years. The cause therefore must be environmental — something that supports test performance of individuals of all genotypes. Several hypotheses have been proposed to explain this. It could be due to the fact that people today are better nourished and better educated, or that modern culture values and supports test-taking skills, or that electronic media stimulate the brain.

Whatever the cause or causes, the result is that modern brains overall are

Gene/environment interactions

By now the reader should be convinced that genes and environment are both critical. Without environment, an organism could not exist because it is from the environment that it obtains the essential materials enabling it to grow and survive, such as nutrients, oxygen, and water. Without genes, an organism could not exist because it would not have the mechanism to extract what it needs from the environment.

It is not about nature versus nurture, as that old cliché would have it. It is about nature-on-nurture-on-nature-on-nurture, round and round and round.

The term for this complex exchange of reciprocating influence is gene/environment interaction. It is not so simple a concept as milk and eggs poured into one mixing bowl. Rather, the two act upon and with each other. The same genotype in different environments may lead to similar or different phenotypes. The same environment operating upon different genotypes may also lead to similar or different phenotypes. Different genotypes in different environments may lead to similar or different phenotypes. It all depends upon interactions.

Here's an example of how gene/environment interaction can play out in real life. There is a gene, ALDH-2, whose protein product helps metabolize alcohol. Some people have an allele for ALDH-2 that is less effective: alcohol byproducts remain in the tissues instead of being metabolized properly. A person with this allele is more likely to become flushed, dizzy, and nauseous in response to drinking. It is estimated that 50 percent of Asian people have an ineffective ALDH-2 allele.

Overall, Asian immigrants to America drink much less alcohol than their children born and raised in the States.

The two genetically similar generations have different drinking patterns for a cultural (that is, environmental) reason: the younger generation is brought up in a culture that places greater emphasis on alcohol.

Studies show that Asian Americans with the less active ALDH-2 allele, both immigrant and first-generation, drink less than their counterparts who have an alternate version of the gene. But there is less of a difference in drinking level between those with and without the special allele in the immigrant generation compared to their children's generation. This is because members of the immigrant generation tend to drink little in any event — whether it makes them sick or not. Both genes and environment affect alcohol consumption, but at different rates under different circumstances.[2]

People who have a particular allele for the gene called ALDH-2 experience a harsh physical reaction when they consume alcohol. It is estimated that up to half of Asian people have this ALDH-2 allele. Whether they choose to drink or not is shaped by other factors. For example, some people may decide that the social pleasures of drinking override its unpleasant side effects.

In a Ray Bradbury short story, a time traveler to the age of dinosaurs accidentally steps on a butterfly, thus altering the course of future events. This story illustrates how small and unpredictable events can cumulatively have significant effects. In behavioral genetics, this concept is called "developmental noise."

Developmental noise

Complicating the process of gene/environment interaction is something called developmental noise. By this is meant the variation introduced by minute, random events that occur during development and have significant cumulative effects on the phenotype.

In a classic science fiction story, a group of hunters time-travel back millions of years to hunt dinosaurs. Their tour guide pre-selects dinosaurs for the kill who are just about to die from other causes, so as not to alter the past. But one of the hunters accidentally steps on a butterfly and kills it. When the group travels forward again to their own time, everything about their world has changed ever so slightly. Just one butterfly died, but generations of offspring never came into exis-tence, triggering a chain of events that shaped a different future.[3]

In the same way, unique and unpredictable events occur inside each cell. An extra dollop of mineral is taken up by one cell, while a molecule of vitamin fails to reach the cell next door: These kinds of tiny, unpredictable variations cause cells to develop differently though they share the same function, genotype, and external environment. It all adds up to make observable differences in the whole organism.

Developmental noise affects physical characteristics such as the number of hairs in an eyebrow or the coloring of a patch of skin. Likewise, developmental noise can have subtle but far-reaching effects on behavior.

Gene/environment correlations

Another factor shaping behavior is gene/environment correlation. A gene/environment correlation occurs when individuals with a genetic propensity for a trait live in environments that support expression of the trait. This kind of correlation can occur in two ways, passive and active.

Suppose a young girl who is genetically gifted for music is born into a talented family of musicians (for sake of argument, let's gloss over the meaning of "genetically gifted for music"). She is surrounded by family members who practice and perform. Her home is filled with instruments, and music plays on the radio all day long. The girl is raised in a home that supports the flourishing of her musical ability. This is an example of a passive gene/environment correlation.

Suppose a boy who is genetically gifted for music is born into a nonmusical family. As a youngster, his parents take him to a parade. He is so excited by the marching band that he persuades his parents to let him take drum lessons. In high school, he joins the orchestra and chooses music electives. He applies to and receives a scholarship to an elite music school. The boy seeks out activities that support the flourishing of his musical ability. This is an example of an active gene/environment correlation.

The above examples show positive correlations, but negative ones may occur: the musically gifted girl who resists the path laid out by her musical family, for example. Positive gene/environment correlations increase the range of phenotypic variation stemming from a given genotype, while negative correlations decrease the range.

Shared and nonshared environments

Does growing up in the same home with the same parents, same physical surroundings, and same everyday experiences make you turn out like your siblings? Does having different friends make you different from your siblings?

Let's take a closer look at the first question. Growing up together in the same home — which falls into a category called shared environment — does make siblings similar in terms of the cultural traditions they inherit: similar in terms of language, modes of dress, diets, and so on.

However, many studies suggest that shared home environment does not do very much to make siblings resemble each other in terms of personality and actions. Each child turns into a distinct character who behaves in individual fashion, despite parents' efforts to raise all their children impartially and despite similarities in genotypes of the siblings (remember that biological siblings are half alike genetically, on average, and twins are fully alike genetically except for a few differences caused by mutation and epigenetic factors).

Some people may be musically gifted, but we do not yet have sufficient scientific data to explain any relationship between genes and talent. We can say, however, that musical *skill* emerges from the interaction of genes and environments.

Now consider the second question. Your unique set of friends is just one example of the many, many experiences that you do not share with a sibling. These experiences contribute to what is called your non-shared environment. Other examples of unique, idiosyncratic non-shared experiences include your prenatal life, your birth, your childhood illnesses and accidents, your particular combination of teachers, your summer camps, and so forth, on through life.

Say that when you turn seven, you undergo the Roman Catholic ritual of First Communion just as all your siblings did when they each turned seven. Although to some degree this is a shared experience, it falls into the category of non-shared environment to the extent that your communion takes place in a unique point in historical time and at a unique moment in your life, with a unique set of other communicants, before a unique congregation, etc., etc.

Such incongruity has led scientists to redefine shared environment. They say it is one that works to make those who experience it similar for a particular trait. By the same token, they have redefined nonshared environment to be one that works to make those who experience it dissimilar for that trait. Some scientists are troubled by the seeming circularity in these definitions; the definition problem underscores the difficulties that environment presents for researchers.

In any event, it doesn't take much imagination to recognize that the number of nonshared environmental factors in anyone's life is so large that together they must have some impact. And indeed, from behavioral genetic studies it appears that the nonshared environment has a significant effect on behavior; it is possibly more significant than genes or shared environments.

But since much of the nonshared environment is random, accidental, and unsystematic, it may well defy study. This makes things difficult for researchers.

Some scientists are working on developing a theory of the envirome (the environment surrounding and affecting a genome) so that it can be studied with the same precision as the genome. Environmental factors, whether shared or nonshared, do not lie on anything so

Many children attend summer camp, yet each child uniquely responds to and is affected by this episode of early life. Summer camp, therefore, is both a shared and non-shared experience.

tangible as a DNA strand; this makes them hard to discern. They are essentially infinite; this makes the job difficult to finish. The big question is, what environmental factors are relevant, discrete, and measurable: socioeconomic status? birth order? number of books in the home? occupation of parents? climate? prevailing attitudes in one's social milieu? Mapping the envirome is such a formidable task that some dismiss it as a hopelessly naïve endeavor. And yet researchers chip away at it.

Heritability
(and environmentability)

In the meantime, the field relies on a less sophisticated tool, a simple mathematical formula that produces a heritability estimate. Heritability is the proportion of phenotypic variation in a population that is due to genetic variation. Some researchers also use the word environmentability to describe heritability's counterpart, that is, the proportion of phenotypic variation in a population that is due to environmental variation. The heritability and environmentability for any given trait are proportions that together add up to 100 percent.

Here are three simple examples that demonstrate heritability. Example 1: The heritability of having a brain in any population of humans is 0, because everyone has a brain; there is no phenotypic variation. Example 2: The heritability of height in a malnourished population — where everyone's growth is stunted — will be lower (closer to zero) than in another population that is well nourished — where everybody's genetic potential can be realized. In both Example 1 and Example 2, zero and low heritability occur even though genes play a critical role in development and growth. Example 3: The heritability of blood type in a random human population approaches 1. The phenotypic variation is mainly attributable to genetic variation. Note that this does not reveal anything about the particular blood type of any individual person in the group.

Heritability is a slippery, confusing concept. Because "heritability" sounds like "inherited," heritability figures are often misconstrued as describing an individual's chances for inheriting a trait, even though heritability is a measure that applies only to groups. Another problem with the concept is that sometimes when the word "heritable" is used to describe a trait, it is misunderstood to mean unchangeable. Yet near-sightedness is both a heritable trait and fixable through eyeglasses, contact lenses, and laser surgery.

For scientists, heritability estimates are unsatisfactory. They are, after all, simply estimates. They apply only to the population being studied in one particular environment and at one point in time. They do not reveal anything about the specific genetic and environmental factors underlying a trait. And yet heritability estimates have their value.

Vision is a heritable trait. It varies phenotypically among humans, which means that everyone does not see equally well. Instead, human eyesight ranges from very poor to excellent. If science advances to the point where all vision deficiencies are corrected by lenses and surgery, then vision would no longer be a heritable trait.

It is possible, through a type of study that will be described in Chapter 4, to come up with a heritability estimate for a trait that looks like this: additive genetic influence, .xx; nonadditive genetic influence, .xx; shared environment, .xx; and nonshared environment, .xx — with all the .xx's adding up to 1.0 or 100 percent.

By calculating such estimates, researchers have learned what we reported in our introduction — that essentially all behavioral traits have a genetic component — and also what we reported earlier in this chapter – that nonshared environments have significant influence on a trait compared to the genes and the shared environment. By repeated application of this tool across similar studies, researchers also have learned that heritability of a trait can change (though for many traits it remains stable both across populations and over time). Heritability measures also have been used to direct research toward those traits that in some contexts are highly heritable — the theory being that genes contributing to such traits may be more susceptible to discovery.

Skip's regrets

Skip, the despondent assistant restaurant manager, wonders why he is such a failure. Is it the fault of the qualities he was born with? Can he blame his mother? Is he a victim of circumstance? Could it be — as harsh as it sounds — his own fault?

A possible clue to this conundrum comes from honeybees. In any honeybee colony, there is only one queen. She is very much larger than all the others, and her function is to lay the eggs. The worker bees tend to the queen, take care of the young, fetch the nectar, and keep the hive maintained.

From the queen's fertilized eggs come the next generation of workers and the future queen. From a cluster of eggs, just one will grow into a mature queen that looks and behaves quite differently from all other bees.

Scientists have wondered how one bee becomes queen and other genetically similar bees do not — as Skip would put it, how one bee turns into a "somebody" and the others remain "losers." Using a relatively new technique to study DNA, scientists recently learned what happens inside the cells of bees to create difference in status. They have discovered that diet makes the difference. Larvae develop into workers when they are fed nectar and pollen. Larvae develop into queens when fed royal jelly, a substance secreted from the glands of worker bees.

Depending on the nutrition each bee receives in the larval stage (an environmental input), certain genes are switched on (through epigenetic effects) that influence development (by coding for particular amino acids). Scientists have found seven different genes in honeybees that are activated differentially by nutrition, though they suspect many more are involved. The question not answered in this research is how worker bees choose which larvae to supply with royal jelly and which to feed the commonplace diet of nectar and pollen.[4]

Scientists pursuing another recent line of research have uncovered a second honeybee phenotype switch. Female honeybees graduate from hive-keepers into foragers, usually at about two weeks of age. This job change has been tracked to the effect of a single gene. The same gene exists in fruit flies, and it determines whether a fly seeks out food near home or searches in a wider range. Further study is needed to discover what triggers the genes to trigger the change in behavior.

Researchers believe that the same gene may operate in humans, though they can only speculate as to the behavior it affects.[5]

The ability of insects with similar genotypes to acquire substantially different phenotypes under different environmental conditions occurs not only in honeybees, but also in other social insects such as ants and termites. Nutrition, temperature, day length, and other environmental factors interact with the genes of these insects to affect phenotypes. Several species of butterfly change wing color with the changing seasons. Dung beetles grow horns or not, depending on their diet. Many such examples can be found in nature.

Scientists believe that a honeybee's occupation, such as hive-keeper or forager, may be determined by epigenetic factors switching a gene on and off. Human occupations are not decided in such a biological manner.

Developmental pathways

The route from egg to larva to worker or queen is called a developmental pathway. Somehow, Skip's developmental pathway has taken him to a place he does not enjoy. He has not become a leader like a queen honeybee. He has not even climbed up the career ladder like the worker bee promoted from hive-keeper to forager. The bees at least are part of a social group, but Skip feels lonely and alone.

Alas, Skip cannot know what went wrong in his life by looking at honeybees. There is no human equivalent to royal jelly that, had his mother fed it to him, would have turned him into a great achiever. Human occupations are not decided at the whim of a few genes triggered on or off. Changing seasons and changes in diet do not determine the human ability to make wise relationship decisions.

Unlike honeybees, humans — at least in free societies — have options. Certainly humans have consciousness — a sense of existence within a surrounding, a sense of being able to take action.

Skip remembers that when he was a child his mother used to say, "If pigs had wings they would fly." That was her way of telling him not to pine for what he does not have. Science cannot tell Skip precisely which environmental inputs could have been put into place to stimulate which epigenetic effects to trigger which genes for which amino acids that would combine to make which proteins that would have made him more successful and happier. Even if he knew all that, Skip could not change his past.

However, Skip can make use of the scientific metaphor of complexity. At age 32, he still has time to move forward on his developmental path. Science cannot advise him on what to do to improve himself, but he has a thinking mind; he can consider his assets and his available choices.

Skip has now what he did not have before: wisdom earned through experience and a desperate resolve to change. What he needs is some self-respect. He should remember that all human beings are genetically similar, just as the honeybees in a hive are. Skip has always had the inborn potential to turn out differently — to become better. He still has it.

The developmental pathway of any living organism continues throughout life. Through their conscious behavior, humans are able to exert at least some control over their destinies.

Notes

1   Clausen *et al.* (1948).

2   See Carey (2003, pgs. 78-79) for discusson of ALDH-2 research.

3   Ray Bradbury's "A Sound of Thunder" (1952).

4   Evans, J. D. and D. E. Wheeler (1999).

5   Ben-Shahar, Y., *et al.* (2002).

RESOURCES FOR CHAPTER 3

Angier, N. 2002. "Honeybee shows a little gene activity goes miles and miles." *New York Times* 7 May, F-3.

Ben-Shahar, Y., A. Robichon, M. B. Sokolowski, G. E. Robinson. 2002. "Influence of gene action across different time scales on behavior." *Science* 296: 741-744.

Biological Sciences Curriculum Study (BSCS). 2000. *Genes, environment, and human behavior.* Colorado Springs: BSCS.

Brown, P. "Brain Gain." 2 March, 2002. *New Scientist* 24-27.

Burghes, A. H. M., H. E. F. Vaessin, A. de la Chapelle. 2001. "The land between Mendelian and multifactorial inheritance." *Science* 293: 2213-2214.

Carey, G. 2003. *Human genetics for the social sciences.* Thousand Oaks, CA: Sage Publications.

Clark, W. and M. Grunstein. 2000. *Are we hardwired? The role of genes in human behavior.* New York: Oxford University Press.

Clausen, J., D. D. Keck, and W. M. Hisesy. 1948. *Experimental studies on the nature of species. III. Environmental responses of climactic races of Achillea.* Carnegie Institute Publication No. 581, Washington, D. C.

Evans, J. D. and D. E. Wheeler. 1999. "Differential gene expression between developing queens and workers in the honey bee, apis mellifera." *Proceedings of the National Academy of Sciences* 96: 5575-5580.

Gottesman, I. 2002. "Nature-nurture controversy," in Brenner, S. and J. H. Miller (eds.), *Encyclopedia of Genetics.* London: Academic Press. Vol. 3, pp. 1297-1302.

Moczek, A. P. 2002. "Research interests/Research system and approaches." University of Arizona/Tucson Nagy Research Center (accessed 6 May); available at http://www.mcb.arizon.a.edu/nagy/moczekresearch.html.

National Institutes of Health. 2000. *NIH consensus statement: Phenylketonuria (PKU): Screening and management.* 17, No. 3.

Pennisi, E. 2002. "One gene determines bee social status." *Science* 296: 636.

Plomin, R., J. C. DeFries, G. E. McClearn, and M. Rutter. 1997. *Behavioral genetics,* 3rd ed. New York: Freeman Press.

Schaffner, K. Forthcoming. "Behaving: Its Nature and Nurture," in Parens, E., A. Chapman, and N. Press (eds.), *Wrestling with Behavioral Genetics: Implications for Understanding Selves and Society.*

"Seasonal polyphenism in butterfly wings." 2002. (accessed 6 May); available at http://www.devbio.com/article.php?ch=22&id=212.

Turkheimer, E. 2000. "Three laws of behavior genetics and what they mean." *Current Directions in Psychological Science* 9: 160-164.

Withgott, J. 1999. "Genes for queens: Understanding more about bee genetics." University of Arizona College of Agriculture and Life Sciences 1999 Arizona Agricultural Experiment Station Research Report. (accessed 6 May); available at http://www.ag.arizona.edu/pubs/general/resrpt1999/beegenetics.pdf.

chapter four

HOW IS GENETIC RESEARCH ON BEHAVIOR CONDUCTED?

■ ■ ■ Anja, an identical twin

Anja has an identical twin sister, Anke, who looks so much like her that they have trouble telling who's who in childhood photographs. Anja and her twin have the same curly brown hair, the same charming grin, and the same lanky bodies. Both are left-handed, nearsighted, and allergic to cats. In many such ways the twins are physically alike.

Yet if you stand the twins side by side, you can find physical distinctions. Anja has a light-brown birthmark near her left ear that Anke does not, and she is a half inch shorter than her sister.

There are non-physical differences, too. Anja is a professional writer while her twin works in graphic design. Anja likes her cup of coffee in the morning while her sister starts the day with diet cola. Anja likes to run for her exercise, and Anke prefers to swim. Anja dresses more conservatively than her sister, but is politically more liberal. Anja has a dry sense of humor, yet her twin is the one who tells outrageously funny stories.

Sometime when Anja is talking with her twin and they both start to say the same thing at the same moment, she wonders what makes them think so much alike. Other times, such as when Anke shows up wearing a new tattoo or puts another pro-gun bumper sticker on her truck, Anja wonders why they think so differently. She knows that their identical genes make them look almost identical. But why don't those identical genes make their minds identical, too?

The fruit fly *Drosophila melano-gaster* is tiny (about 3 mm long) and short-lived (about 2 weeks). However, its petite size and quick life cycle, plus its non-fussy eating habits, make it the ideal study organism for behavioral geneticists.

Animal studies

The "teacher's pet" of behavioral genetic research is the common fruit fly, *Drosophila melanogaster*, and some 2,000 related species. The fruit fly is a favorite of researchers for simple reasons. Fruit flies are easy to collect and keep: just bait a jar with overripe fruit and trap them. They reproduce rapidly and copiously; the time span from egg to adult is less than two weeks and one female produces hundreds of offspring. Fruit flies willingly cooperate in researchers' efforts to selectively breed them and to run them through all sorts of experiments. What's more, fruit flies do not bite and do not transmit disease to humans, and researchers do not need to obtain government approval to ensure that the research protects the flies' rights and privacy.

Basic genetic research on fruit flies started more than 100 years ago, but the classic study on behavior dates to the 1950s. Researchers noticed that if you put fruit flies in a tilting maze, some would crawl upward and others would crawl downward. This tendency to move with or against gravity is called geotaxis.

The researchers selected fruit flies that preferred to move uphill and bred them together and did the same for fruit flies that preferred to move downhill. When after many generations they had created strains of fruit flies that consistently responded to gravity in the same way, the researchers were able to conclude that there was a genetic basis to geotaxis. This selective breeding experiment contributed early evidence to the claim that heredity plays a role in behavioral traits.

The mice and rabbit studies described in Chapter 2 and many others like them were all modeled after this original fruit fly experiment. Bacteria, yeast, shrimp, moths, spiders, mosquitoes, ants, snails, cats, and dogs are just a few of the many other species that have served as subjects for behavioral genetic research.

When they study animals, genetic researchers frame questions in terms of *variations* in behavior among individuals within a species. They explore such questions as:

- How do bacteria vary in their use of the little whips, called flagellae, by which they propel themselves?
- How do worms vary in their response to stimuli such as touch, taste, smell, and temperature?
- How do variations in the trilling calls of male crickets affect their attractiveness to female crickets?
- How do bee species differ in the ratio of pollen to nectar they collect?
- How do fish vary in their use of specific courtship rituals such as swinging, sidling, nibbling, pecking, and thrusting?
- How does the variation in feather color, plumage, and body outline of male chickens affect their attractiveness to females?
- How do rats differ in play, how do pigs differ in responses to stress, and how do chimpanzees differ in personality?

As this partial list suggests, questions about behavior are endless. One way such questions are researched is through breeding experiments already described, in which researchers create distinct lines that consistently and reliably diverge in behavior on a particular trait despite minimal environmental variation.

Another method is to create inbred strains. These are whole populations of genetically near-identical animals that have been created by mating brothers to sisters for a number of generations. (In recent years researchers have learned how to make inbred strains through cloning.) Researchers look for variations in behavior between different inbred strains reared in identical environments, as evidence of genetic components to behavior. They also look for variations in behavior *within* inbred strains. Since members of an in-bred strain are genetically alike, observed differences in behavior can be attributed to pre- or postnatal environmental causes.

Animals make excellent research studies not merely because they can be bred at will and kept in controlled environments. Another reason they are so suitable is that, as mentioned in Chapter 2, their genomes are related to ours. When researchers discover the function and location of genes associated with behavioral traits in animals, they have clues as to the function and location of genes associated with related behavioral traits in humans. Such research requires species-specific genome maps and knowledge of which regions correspond across species.

Cloned animals allow researchers to observe how organisms with identical genes develop differently. This provides clues as to the interactive effects of the environment on genes.

Family Studies

A fundamental experimental method involving humans is the family study. This starts with one person, called the proband, and the focus is on one particular trait possessed by that person. The proband's family tree (pedigree) is drawn up to include first-degree relatives (parents, siblings, and children) and sometimes also second-degree relatives (aunts, uncles, grandchildren, grandparents, and nephews or nieces), plus even more distant family members. The members of the family tree are looked at to see who, if anyone, has the trait identified in the proband or related traits.

This type of study can reveal whether the trait runs in the family. It does not explain *why*. Both genes and environment are implicated because the members of a biological family are similar genetically and also tend to live in similar environments. However, it is sometimes possible to get a clue about cause from a family study. For example, if a proband has a trait in common with first-degree relatives and also with more distant relatives, the possibility is raised that the cause comes from the environment shared by the family rather than shared genes.

Twin Studies

In twin studies, researchers actively recruit living twins. They observe the twins' behaviors, give them personality tests, interview them, and ask them to fill out surveys. Researchers also extract data on twins from existing databanks, such as records on hospital patients or members of the armed forces.

Twin studies rely on the fact that identical (MZ or monozygotic) twins have essentially the same set of genes while fraternal (DZ or dizygotic) twins have, on average, a half-identical set. A basic assumption in these studies is that since pairs of both types are raised alongside each other, both types are affected by their environments to an equal degree. In other words, the environment of an identical twin pair is not working to make

Scientists refer to identical twins as MZ twins (for monozygotic, meaning developing from a single fertilized egg), because they are not truly identical, not even genetically. Developmental and epigenetic factors cause each twin's genes to be slightly unique and to operate in unique fashion.

those two alike to any greater degree than the environment of a fraternal twin pair makes those two alike. The single factor making identical twins more alike compared to fraternal twins is their greater genetic similarity. This is called the equal environments assumption.

Given this assumption, twin pairs may be examined for a particular trait such as autism, scores on a personality test, or educational attainment. Data from many twin pairs are collected and the rates of similarity for identical and fraternal pairs are then compared.

If the trait under study is discrete — either present or absent, such as a disease — concordance rates are calculated. This is the proportion of the twin pairs that both have the trait under study. If the trait under study is continuous — appearing to different degrees in individuals, such as height or I.Q. — then a correlation coefficient is calculated. This number reflects the extent to which the measurement or score for one twin predicts the measurement or score for the second twin.

Here's how twin study findings are analyzed:

- Genetic influence is indicated when the concordance rate or correlation coefficient for identical twins exceeds that for fraternal twins;
- Shared environmental influences are indicated when the similarity for both types of twins are quite close (and significantly more than zero); and
- Non-shared environmental influences

are indicated when identical twins are dissimilar for a trait.

In the typical twin study, all three sources of influence are operating simultaneously, but can be teased apart and given "weights" by combining data from family strategies.

Here are two examples. A study on male homosexuality and bisexuality produced a concordance rate of .52 for identical twins and .22 for fraternal twins (it can help to read a correlation of .52 as "52 percent").[1] It has been found that identical twins have a correlation of .96 for the ridge pattern in their fingerprints while fraternal twins have a correlation of .47.[2]

Note that in the first example, the concordance rate for identical twins was not

Fraternal or DZ (dizygotic) twins typically are born at the same time and are raised very similarly, just like identical twins, but they are only about half alike genetically. Scientists look at how a particular behavior trait varies between pairs of identical twins and pairs of fraternal twins to mathematically estimate how genes (and by inference, environments) affect that behavior.

1.0 and the concordance rate for fraternal twins was not .5. This suggests that homosexuality and bisexuality are not purely determined by genetics. Note in the second example how much closer the correlation rates are to 1.0 percent and .5, respectively. This suggests that the physical features of a fingerprint are very highly determined by one's genetic make-up.

Heritability estimates also are derived from twin studies. As explained in Chapter 3, such estimates are based on ratios: the relationship between the phenotypic (observable) variation of the trait in twin pairs and the genetic variation for those twin pairs. Ratios for identical twins and fraternal twins are compared to calculate heritability.

In the sexuality study quoted above, the researchers estimated heritability for male homosexuality and bisexuality of between .31 and .74. Notice how broad that range is. It suggests that the variation

in sexual orientation in the male population is anywhere from under one-third to just about two-thirds a factor of heredity. This leaves ample room for influential environmental effects.

Adoption Studies

Adoption studies look at biologically related people who have been reared apart. One method is to compare identical twins adopted into separate homes, that is, into measurably dissimilar environments. The disparate environments are assumed to shape them differently so that similarities in traits are attributed, at least in part, to genetic effects.

Another method compares adopted children to both their biological and adoptive parents. Evidence for partial genetic influence on a trait is found when adoptees are more similar for the trait to their biological parents than to their adoptive parents. Evidence for some environmental influence is found when the adoptee is more like his or her adoptive parents than the biological parents.

Yet another adoption method is to compare adopted children to other children in the family who are biological offspring of the parents. Similarity found here would suggest environmental effects for the trait under investigation, while dissimilarity would suggest genetic effects.

Adoption studies are not as numerous as family or twin studies because subjects are hard to find, especially given the

Scientists learn about the genetic influence on behavior (and by inference, the environmental influence on behavior) by comparing the traits of biologically related siblings, non-biologically related siblings, parents and their children (related biologically and not), adoptive and biological parents and their children, and other combinations.

decline in within-nation adoption over the past several decades. Also, in countries such as the United States where adoption records are confidential, it can be difficult for researchers to get accurate information about the biological parents.

Combined studies

We have described family, twin, and adoption studies as distinct types of research, but in practice they can overlap. As just noted, an adoption study might look at pairs of twins that had been adopted away into different families. Some studies have unusual permutations, for example, a family study might include stepchildren who are related to one but not both parents.

Furthermore, data from all three kinds of studies can be pooled together. This kind of undertaking, called meta-analysis, attempts to extract more meaning out of data that have been generated by multiple studies of the same trait. In a mathematical exercise called model fitting, several plausible explanations, in the form of mathematical formulas, are proposed that express the relative contributions of genetics and environment to the variance for a trait. The combined data are plugged into each model to see which one best explains the variance.

One of the problems confronted by model fitters is that different studies might use different diagnostic measures to identify those who have or do not have the trait under study. For example, a subject who is gauged as "highly religious" in one study might not be so categorized in another. Therefore, researchers must assume degrees of error and hope that the signal outweighs the noise.

Today, researchers attempt to be consistent with each other in their data collection methods. They collaborate on diagnostic measures and study designs with the intention of eventually pooling their data for meta-analysis. Several such projects are underway involving teams across the country and around the world. These studies are investigating schizophrenia and other mental illnesses, alcoholism, autism, and many other behavioral disorders.

Linkage analysis

The traditional way that behavior has been studied by geneticists using twin, family, and adoption studies is referred to as quantitative research, because the objective is to identify how behavioral traits vary by degree (quantitatively) in individuals in a population. Molecular research, which probes at the DNA level, complements this classical approach. Such research makes use of the tremendous computing power that has come about in recent years. It also takes advantage of the completed drafts of human, animal, and insect DNA sequences achieved through the Human Genome Project and related ventures.

In a meta-analysis study, data from family, twin, and adoption studies on the same trait are pooled together and analyzed, in an attempt to extract more meaning.

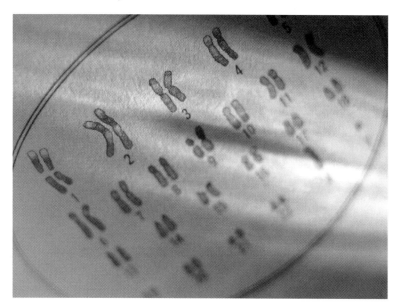

Through increasingly sophisticated techniques, researchers have been able to find the locations of genes within chromosomes and to identify the effects those genes have when activated.

Before the advent of modern molecular genetics, researchers did not have any efficient means for pinpointing the genes that underlie a trait. Their main resource was an approach called linkage analysis that helped them close in on the neighborhood along a chromosome where a gene for a trait might be located.

Linkage analysis relies on the fact that chromosomes are paired. In germ cells, the two chromosomes in a pair commonly exchange genetic material before the full complement of chromosomes splits in half to create the sperm and egg cells of reproduction. This exchange is called recombination or crossing over. Recombination is a normal exchange process, unrelated to mutation, that enhances genetic diversity. It creates new combinations of alleles on each chromosome.

The frequency with which the alleles for two different genes get separated by recombination depends on the distance between the genes. If the two alleles on one chromosome are far apart, one of them is likely to end up on the other chromosome from the pair after recombination. If the two alleles are close together, they are likely to remain on the same chromosome from the pair after recombination. Remember that the two chromosomes of each pair peel off into separate germ cells. The alleles that remain together on one chromosome after recombination will be inherited together. The alleles that end up on different chromosomes will not be inherited together.

In classical linkage analysis, researchers collect data on two variables from family groups. The first variable is the trait being researched. The second variable is called a genetic marker. This is a gene whose precise location on a chromosome is already known. For each family member, researchers record whether and to what extent the trait is present and which allele for the marker gene is present. They note how often the trait and any particular allele for the marker gene are inherited together. Where a pattern of frequency occurs, this suggests that the gene for the trait is near the marker gene ("linked") because the combination of alleles for the two genes (haplotypes) is *not* being broken apart in recombination. Researchers make statistical calculations from their data to come up with a lod score ("lod" stands for "logarithmic odds" or "likelihood of odds"). The higher the lod score, the higher the probability that the two genes are close by on the same chromosome.

Researchers do this type of analysis with several families. They also look for linkage between the gene for the trait under study and several different marker genes. The first tactic helps them confirm linkage and the latter tactic helps them better target the approximate location along the chromosome of the trait-related gene.

Linkage analysis has shortcomings. It does not reveal the precise locations of genes. Furthermore, it is suitable only for one type of gene – what researchers refer to as a major gene. This term describes genes for which an allele, acting by itself, is sufficient to trigger significant and easily observable phenotypic differences in a trait. In humans such genes are primarily associated with health disorders, and so linkage analysis has mainly been applied in the search for the responsible gene in rare single-gene disorders that heavily affect some families, such as Huntington's disease. Classical linkage analysis has much less practical value for researchers studying behavior. This is because in almost all cases, behavior is affected by multiple locus genes — by many genes whose alleles, operating in synchrony, each contribute in some small way to observable differences in a trait.

By 1980, advances in technology had enabled researchers to develop a method for tracking the co-inheritance of a trait with a discrete sequence of DNA in the genome that varies in the population, rather than with an entire gene. (Many such variable DNA sequences exist in the genome of humans and other organisms.) Subsequently, researchers learned how to track the co-inheritance of a trait with single bits of DNA in the genome that vary in a population (these are called SNPs or single nucleotide polymorphisms). This refined search capability of modern linkage analysis has been used to reveal the actual location of many genes along the chromosomes.

Also thanks to technological advances, researchers no longer have to bother with tracking the co-inheritance of a trait with a single marker or SNP at a time. Instead they do whole genome scans. DNA samples are simultaneously read at dozens or more markers or SNPs located along the chromosomes to see if any particular DNA sequence shows up more than randomly in individuals who have the trait. The noun *genotype* is turned into a verb to describe this activity. Genotyping makes it technically feasible to find the location of multiple genes that play minor roles in traits. This kind of research is called QTL analysis. As you may recall, QTL stands for quantitative trait loci. Through QTL analysis, researchers seek the location of the many genes whose alleles, in their many different forms, affect a variable trait.

Association studies

Another molecular research route is the association study. This focuses on a single gene that has already been isolated, the candidate gene. Through the association study, researchers seek to identify whether the variation in this gene's alleles might be statistically associated with variation in a particular trait.

DNA samples are taken from subjects who have the trait and a similar number of subjects (a control group) without the trait. Each subject's DNA is genotyped to see which allele is present at the genetic locus under study. A statistical test is then conducted to see if any allele shows up more frequently in subjects with the trait compared to subjects without the trait.

Association studies have two advantages over linkage analysis. First, they require a smaller number of subjects who do not have to be related. Second, they can help identify specific genes, not just chromosomal regions. This moves researchers that much closer to the next step, which is to figure out how specific genes correlated with a trait contribute to the biological processes underlying that trait.

The complete mapping of the human genome has helped researchers find candidate genes on which to focus their research using the association method. Animal studies also have helped identify good targets for association studies using human subjects. The quantity of association studies churning out from research labs in recent years has been described as a "veritable cascade."[3] These studies cover a broad spectrum of diseases and traits — Parkinson's disease, multiple sclerosis, restless leg syndrome, smoking behavior, and migraines, to name just a few.

Microarray analysis

Recall the quantitative experiments in behavioral genetics involving fruit flies and gravity, described earlier in this chapter. From these experiments researchers knew that genetics was involved in geotaxis, but they could not show how. In 2002 — fifty years after that initial research — scientists were finally able to identify several of the many genes involved in this trait. The molecular technology that allowed them to do this is microarray analysis. This technique is revolutionary because it allows scientists to examine thousands of genes simultaneously.

Here is a simplistic explanation of this complex procedure: an organism's genome is extracted and placed in segments on a chip. The chip is soaked in a solution containing RNA that has been expressed by a particular cell. The solution also contains a fluorescent dye. If a particular gene is expressed in the cell, the RNA from the solution will bind to it. This will cause that particular segment to light up. The more the gene is expressed, the stronger the fluorescence. In the recent fruit fly investigation,

Microarray analysis allows researchers to visually observe expressed genes. This technique is providing important clues about the mysterious relationship between genes and behavior.

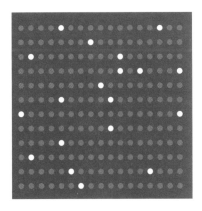

In microarray analysis, genomic material from a cell is placed on a slide soaked in an RNA solution. Genes that are expressed in the cell bind to the RNA, causing a fluorescent reaction.

microarray analysis helped scientists find genes that were expressed in the flies that like to crawl up and in those that like to crawl down.[4]

Researchers also use microarray techniques on humans. For example, they take tissue samples from subjects with and without a mental disorder or some other observable trait. They then compare results from the two types of subjects to learn which genes are involved and their expression patterns. With the increasing popularity of microarray experiments, huge amounts of data are being produced that eventually should lead to a better understanding of how specific genotypes relate to phenotypes.

Knockout studies

One final molecular research method used in behavioral genetics will be described here. This technique has been applied to mice but not to humans, for reasons that will be obvious once you learn about it. It is the knockout study. Researchers use modern laboratory techniques to deactivate a gene in stem cells (undifferentiated cells that can turn into specialized cells). These cells are inserted into an embryo that is then implanted into the womb of a female. After the offspring is born and has matured, its germ cells (sperm or eggs) are examined to see if any evolved from the altered stem cells. Those germ cells are used for breeding to create a line of knockout mice, all missing the target gene.

The knockout mice are studied to see whether their behavior differs from untreated mice. If a behavior is altered when the gene is knocked out, then the gene is implicated. Similar techniques are used to knock in genes. It also is possible through these techniques to add or deactivate even a small segment of DNA in order to determine the function of a gene's component parts. Researchers also can move a gene from one spot in the genome to another to see how location affects expression.

Mice behavior traits that have been studied using this kind of genetic manipulation include movement patterns, willingness to explore, weight retention, learning and memory, social interaction,

Variations in nutrition, education, upbringing, and other aspects of environment help make each human personality unique. Even genetically identical twins have distinct personalities, resulting in large part from environmental effects.

and stress response, among many others. Since mice and humans have similar genomes, researchers hope to obtain from the mice studies clues about corresponding genes in humans.

Anja's Question

Research in behavioral genetics has provided an answer to the question posed by Anja. She is the woman who wonders why her appearance is so very similar to her identical twin's but her behavior is not so much alike.

The answer has two parts. First, the role of genes in physical development is far more direct than it is in behavior. Second, non-shared environmental influences (including chance occurrences) are so great that they cause even closely attached twins to develop personalities as different from each other as those of any ordinary pair of non-twin siblings.

Here's a more detailed explanation. The twins' similar height is a product of skeletal structure (among other things). Scores of genes encode for the amino acids that engender proteins that influence bone length. The work of these genes is affected by their interactions with other genes, their interactions with the environment, developmental noise, and the epigenetic factors that control gene expression.

All sorts of small environmental variables surrounding two genetically equivalent females who are raised similarly

would cause them to end up with slightly different heights. Anja is a little shorter than her sister perhaps because she received a slightly less copious supply of nutrients through her umbilical cord during fetal development, compared to her twin. Perhaps her sister crowded her in the uterus. After birth, she might have had an illness her twin did not have that ever so slightly retarded her growth. Perhaps she did not like milk as a child, and so her body had less calcium with which to build bones in the formative years.

The twins' nearsightedness is a product of their genetic endowment operating in an environment where people spend long hours staring at electronic screens and reading small type. Slight differences in these conditions might cause the twins' eyesights to differ slightly. If there are major environmental differences, such as if one twin contracts a virus that triggers a serious eye infection or if one twin is hit in the eye with a BB gun pellet, there could be a larger difference in their visual abilities.

Anja has a birthmark that her sister does not, and this is explained by developmental noise operating on genetics. Random chance resulted in extra pigment cells clustering near her ear, resulting in the light-brown mark.

A multitude of genes encode for the amino acids that, in chains linked together as proteins, build and maintain the various parts of the brain and their connections and that move nerve impulses throughout the body. These genes, too, are influenced by interactions with other genes, interactions with environmental factors, developmental noise, and epigenetic effects. As a result, the twins have brains that differ in structure and in the neuronal connections through which impulses are processed.

But behavior is a p*roduct* of the brain. Anke's predilection for decorating her body with tattoos, to take one example of a behavioral trait, is mediated in the brain but it is not a *part* of the brain. This magnifies the differences in behavior, because no matter how close any twins are, they uniquely experience the world — their genotype is differently affected by non-shared environmental factors. Each twin's brain is wired somewhat differently, impulses move through their nervous systems somewhat differently, and

different memories are saved and stored. Differences build upon differences to create two unique personalities.

It should be noted that behavior is not exclusively a product of the brain. Other organs play their part, too. For example, your kidneys affect how you handle alcohol and your lungs affect your ability to run. So in parallel to this description of the brain, the many other organs in the respective bodies of Anja and Anke follow unique developmental pathways and thus have different mediating effects on the behavior of each twin.

Concerns about non-molecular research

It would be nice to be able to explain to Anja which specific genetic and environmental variables cause her to either resemble or be distinct from her twin sister. And it would be nice to explain how genes and environments work together to have those effects. But any sort of detailed explanation must wait until the research is much further along. We cannot expect answers, one textbook on behavioral genetics says, "when such research is at the stage of placing one's toes into the pond to test the temperature of the water."[5]

In addition to the large questions of which and how, the field also struggles with basic questions over methodology. Here are some of the questions that have confronted researchers:

Is a tattoo a beautiful adornment or a disfiguring scar? Identical twins may differ in their opinions on the matter, because each has a unique personality shaped by a unique experience of the world.

The twin relationship is sufficiently unusual that some critics question whether conclusions from behavior studies of twins can be applied to the general population. Twin researchers respond that their work often yields results similar to those obtained through other kinds of studies.

How do researchers know that they have correctly categorized identical and fraternal twins? In the past, researchers categorized twins based on visual checks (do they look alike?), physical tests (do they have the same blood type?), and self-reports (do they think they are identical or fraternal?). Today, researchers can use DNA testing to confirm whether twins developed from one or two eggs. Many of the field's original studies do not stand on this level of certainty. Yet they are probably fairly accurate: by conducting DNA checks on twins categorized as identical or fraternal by non-DNA methods, researchers have learned that the latter are correct about 95 percent of the time.

Is the equal environments assumption valid? As we explained earlier, twin studies assume that identical and fraternal twin pairs all experience the same degree of shared environment. But this may not be wholly true. The close resemblance of identical twins may cause them to think of themselves as alike and other people to act towards them as though they were alike. In addition, all identical twin pairs are same-sex (there are very rare exceptions), but a third of all fraternal twin pairs are opposite-sex. These factors could make the environments of identical twins more similar compared to the environments of fraternal twins. Many scientists assert that the equal environments assumption is valid, based on studies conducted specifically to test it, but others remain unconvinced.

Is it valid to generalize from twin studies? Some people say that the twin experience is not typical. Twins have a greater incidence of premature birth and therefore of developmental problems. Also, people tend to treat twins as special and many twins perceive themselves as having a special closeness to each other. These kinds of subtle differences between twins and non-twins suggest that conclusions from studies on the former may not apply to the latter. A point in defense of twin studies is that the data they produce, on many traits, converge with the data produced through other kinds of studies.

Is it valid to generalize from adoption studies? The people involved in adoptions — the children, the biological parents, and the adoptive families — may not be typical of the broader population because they have experienced an unusual family drama. This could limit the relevance of data from adoption studies — but again, the convergence of findings from adoption studies and other forms of research argues against this being an important concern.

Are shared environmental effects adequately controlled for in adoption studies? An assumption underlying many adoption studies is that adoptees are randomly assigned into dissimilar environments and not selectively placed. Based on this assumption, any correlations found between adopted-away identical twins would be due entirely to genetics.

But the fact is that many children are adopted by relatives or into families that are similar in many respects to their biological families. For example, adoption agencies have been known to place a child born to Irish Catholics into an Irish Catholic family in the same city. Some adopted-away twins do not part company until they are a few months or years old; they may experience important stages of their development in a shared environment. All twins, even those adopted away at birth, are together in the womb that at least in part operates as a shared environment. These are three examples of how adopted-away twins may experience environments that are more similar than assumed.

■ *Are non-shared environmental effects adequately controlled for in twin studies?* Although twins develop together in one womb, they experience it differently as they compete for resources. All fraternal twins develop in separate chorionic sacs, and so do some identical twins. These are two examples of how even the prenatal environment can operate as an unaccounted-for non-shared environmental influence.

Obviously it is very difficult to observe and identify all the non-shared environmental factors at work shaping a trait, and yet they may have a much stronger effect than factors of shared environment. As a pair of scientists wrote, "Because these non-shared differences are nonsystematic and largely accidental or random, they are and will continue to be very difficult to study." The scientists called this a "gloomy prospect."[6]

■ *What about non-additive genetic effects?* How do studies on quantitative traits take these into account? Genes do not work simply in an additive way, with each gene contributing to an effect in a separate and measurable way. Genes also have non-additive effects that, as we explained in Chapter 3, fall into two main categories: genotype-environment correlation and genotype-environment interaction. In the past, quantitative studies did not take these into consideration; modern research designs have been better at incorporating measurements of the former than the latter.

An underlying assumption of adoption studies is that children are randomly placed with families. In practice, children may be placed in families that are similar in important ways to their biological family, making it more difficult to determine the degree to which genetic or environmental effects work to influence a trait. Twins researchers say they now recognize non-random placement and take it into account when making their estimations.

Concerns about molecular research

Gene discoveries for all sorts of traits, from grooming to obsessive hand-washing, have been heralded by molecular researchers. Yet most of these claims have not stood up over time. From literally hundreds of molecular studies, only a handful of genes have been solidly identified with a quantitative trait. And none of these confirmed genes has more than a very small effect of the relevant trait's total variation.

Scientists think that the reason there are so few confirmed QTLs is that molecular studies are very difficult to replicate. This is not necessarily because the original studies are faulty — though some claims for allelic associations have been based on low statistical correlations. Replication problems stem mainly from the fact that for statistical reasons a larger pool of subjects is needed to make confir-mations, and these studies are harder to do. Another important reason is that, as we stated before, most genes are of very small effect, and so are simply difficult to identify through molecular means.

The lack of success in confirming QTL claims is one concern that has been raised about molecular research into behavior, but there are other concerns, too. Here are some of the questions that have been raised:

■ *How much insight about human behavior can you get from behavior observed in animals?* Knockout studies provide tempting opportunities to speculate about the role of particular genes in human behavior, but it is a temptation that must be avoided. Suppose, for example, that a knockout study creates mice that run a maze faster. Does this mean similarly affected humans would also run a maze faster? Maze running is not a typical human activity, so what is

What genes affect the ability of humans to run a maze? Researchers cannot look for the answer to that question by conducting knockout studies on human subjects, because that would be unethical. Yet they cannot speculate about human maze-running behavior based on results from studies of knock-out mice, either. This is because the genes shared by humans and other animals express themselves differently and in very different contexts.

the analogous behavior?

The reason it is risky to speculate about such questions is because there are significant differences in how and when genes express themselves in different species. Species also differ in terms of gene-gene and gene-environment interactions. Analogous genetic mutations in animals and humans could have very different effects on protein process, and thus indirectly on behavior.

■ *Do the molecular studies find false positives?* When researchers use genome scans to look for any correlations between a trait and tens of thousands of genes, the possibility always exists of random hits. There also is the possibility of finding a correlation that exists in one population but not in others. The reason for this is that certain alleles appear more frequently in some populations than in others; such numerical counts are called gene frequencies. If researchers designing an association study do not carefully control for population, it may produce false data. Two molecular geneticists in a 1994 article nicely explain this risk; they call it the "chopsticks problem":

> *Suppose that a would-be geneticist set out to study the 'trait' of ability to eat with chopsticks in the San Francisco population by performing an association study with the HLA complex [a set of immune response genes that frequently vary between ethnic groups]. The allele*

HLA-A1 would turn out to be positively associated with ability to use chopsticks – not because immunological determinants play any role in manual dexterity, but simply because the allele HLA-A1 is more common among Asians than Caucasians. [7]

Overcoming the research concerns

Behavioral geneticists have worked tremendously hard to improve their research methods and so improve the quality of the data generated. On the quantitative front, researchers have tried many different techniques to capture the environmental influences that act in concert with genes to influence behaviors. Some researchers have tried counting the number of books in each subject's household, assessing parents' vocabulary,

Gene studies conducted on non-random populations may lead to false conclusions. This is called the "chopsticks problem," after this well-known example: If you conduct a gene study of residents in San Francisco, you might find a gene that correlates with using chopsticks. However, that gene might not have anything remotely to do with utensil habits. It might be related to the fact that most of those studied are of Asian heritage.

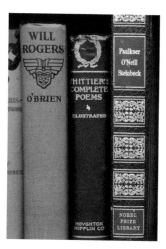

Scientists are grappling with the problem of how to identify and measure the environmental variables that influence behavior. Does the presence or absence of certain objects in the home have an effect? Or are environmental effects not so easily quantified?

noting the availability of such household objects as power tools and dictionaries, or measuring other variables deemed relevant.

Another approach has been to use questionnaires and/or interviews to determine whether identical twins are treated more similarly compared to fraternal twins. Researchers also have studied fraternal twins who look a lot alike to see if they are more concordant than fraternal twins who do not resemble each other. Piece by piece these efforts are resulting in better and more useful data, but they also serve to underline the difficulty of accounting for all the truly pertinent environmental factors.

On the molecular front, researchers are increasing sample sizes and improving statistical methods. The astounding advances in microarray technology have allowed researchers to target ever-smaller regions of DNA while scanning ever-larger segments of the genome simultaneously; over time this should improve the

yield for "gene hunters" while reducing the number of false positives. Meanwhile, scientists as a whole have become more cautious about issuing speculative claims about genes based on unreplicated work.

Another exciting development has come about with the introduction into the behavioral genetics lab of sophisticated brain imaging tools. These tools allow researchers to observe the brain activity that occurs in organisms when specific genes are expressed in controlled environments.

Yet the increasing sophistication of molecular research serves to underscore the truly monumental tasks of behavioral genetics. As one scientist has summed up the state of affairs: "Researchers have been creative in developing new theories, measuring tools, statistical programs, etc. But the constant retooling of approaches points to the extraordinary complexity of trying to dissect out the environmental, genetic, stochastic and personal parameters in the development of behaviors in human beings."[8]

Notes

1   See Bailey, J. M. and Pillard, R. C. (1991).

2   Falconer, D. S. and T. F. C. Mackay (1996, p. 173).

3   Bird, T. D. *et al.* (2001, p. 1153).

4   See Toma, D. P. *et al.* (2002).

5   See Carey, G. (2002, pg. 6).

6   Plomin, R. and D. David (1987, pg. 8).

7   See Lander, E. S. and N. J. Schork (1994, p. 2041). Also cited in Schaffner, K. (forthcoming).

8   Beckwith, J. (forthcoming).

RESOURCES FOR CHAPTER 4

Bailey, J. M., and R. C. Pillard. 1991. "A genetic study of male sexual orientation." *Archives of General Psychiatry* 48: 1089-96.

Beckwith, J. Forthcoming. "Whither human behavioral genetics?" in Parens, E., A. Chapman, and N. Press (eds.), *Wrestling with Behavioral Genetics: Implications for Understanding Selves and Society*.

Bird, T. D., G. P. Jarvik, N. W. Wood. 2001. "Genetic association studies: Genes in search of diseases." *Neurology* 57: 1153-1154.

Biological Sciences Curriculum Study (BSCS). 2000. *Genes, environment, and human behavior*. Colorado Springs: BSCS.

Carey, G. 2003. *Human genetics for the social sciences*. Thousand Oaks, CA: Sage Publications.

Cooper, N., ed. 1992. "The Human Genome Project." *Los Alamos Science*: 20.

Egan, M., M. Kojima, J. Callicott, T. E. Goldberg, B.S. Kolachana, A. Bertolino, E. Zaitsev, B. Gold, D. Goldman, M. Dean, B. Lu and D. R. Weinberger. 2002. "5HT1Db receptor gene implicated in the pathogenesis of obsessive-compulsive disorder: Further evidence from a family-based association study." *Molecular Psychiatry* 7: 805-809.

Ehrlich, P., and M. Feldman. 2003. "Genes and culture: what creates our behavioral phenome?" *Cultural Anthropology* 44: 87-107.

Ehrman, L. 2004. *Behavior genetics*. New York: Oxford University Press.

Falconer, D. S. and T. F. C. MacKay. 1996. *Introduction to Quantitative Genetics*, 4th ed. Reading, MA: Addison-Wesley Publishing Company.

Greer, J.M., and M. R. Capecchi. 2002. "*Hoxb8* is required for normal grooming behavior in mice." *Neuron* 33: 23-34.

Hamer, D. 2002. "Rethinking behavior genetics." *Science* 298: 71-72.

Lander, E.S., and N. J. Schork. 1994. "Genetic dissection of complex traits: guidelines for interpreting and reporting linkage results." *Nature Genetics* 11: 241-7.

Mundo, E., M. A. Richter, G. Zai, F. Sam, J. McBride, F. Macciardi, and J. L. Kennedy. 2002. "5HT1D gene implicated in the pathogenesis of Obsessive-Compulsive Disorder: Further evidence from a family-based association study." *Molecular Psychiatry* 7: 805-809.

Neiderhiser, J. 2001. "Understanding the roles of genome and envirome: Methods in genetic epidemiology." *British Journal of Psychiatry* 178 (suppl. 40): s12-s17.

Nuffield Council on Bioethics. 2002. *Genetics and human behaviour*. London: Nuffield Council on Bioethics.

Plomin, R. 2003. "Genetics, genes, genomics, and g." *Molecular Psychiatry* 8: 1-5.

Plomin, R., J. C. DeFries, G. E. McClearn, and M. Rutter. 1997. *Behavioral genetics*, 3rd ed. New York: Freeman Press.

Plomin, R., and D. Daniels. 1987. "Why are children in the same family so different from one another?" *Behavioral and Brain Sciences* 10: 1-60.

Schaffner, K. Forthcoming. "Behaving: its nature and nurture." in Parens, E., A. Chapman, and N. Press (eds.), *Wrestling with Behavioral Genetics: Implications for Understanding Selves and Society*.

Sherman, S., J. C. DeFries, I. I. Gottesman, J. C. Loehlin, J. M. Meyer, M. Z. Pelias, J. Rice, and I. Waldman. 1997. "Recent developments in human behavioral genetics: Past accomplishments and future directions." *American Journal of Human Genetics* 60: 1265-1275.

Toma, D., K. White, J. Hirsch, R. Greenspan. 2002. "Identification of genes involved in drosophila melanogaster geotaxis, a complex behavioral trait." *Nature Genetics* 31: 349-353.

chapter five

HOW DO MENTAL DISORDERS EMERGE FROM THE MIX OF GENES AND ENVIRONMENTS?

■ ■ ■ Lamar, a man with bad news

Lamar is sitting in a coffee shop, stunned. His fiancée Marta has just broken up with him. She gave him some odd reasons. "It's important for me to have children and I don't think you should have them," she said. She also said, "I don't think I'll be able to take care of you." Before Lamar could respond, Marta fled from the restaurant.

At first Lamar couldn't make sense of her remarks. Then it occurred to him that this unhappy scene might be connected to the drama already taking place in his family.

About a month ago, Lamar and Marta had plans to meet his mother Adele for dinner at a new restaurant outside of town. Adele never showed up. Lamar spent several hours calling and driving around, trying to locate her. Finally, near midnight, his mother called him from a pay phone. She had no idea where she was or how she had gotten there.

This was not the first time Adele had gotten lost, but before she had always blamed it on being distracted and terrible with directions. This time Lamar did not buy the excuses. He insisted she go to her doctor.

After a thorough exam and several diagnostic tests, Adele was given a dreadful diagnosis. She has Alzheimer's disease. With this illness, plaques and tangles (two types of protein residue) build up in the brain, destroying cells. Over the course of years, people with Alzheimer's lose memory, reasoning and language abilities, and their independence. Eventually the brain is unable to carry out basic tasks, causing death. Alzheimer's usually strikes people over age sixty-five, but some forms, known as early-onset Alzheimer's, strike people even younger. Adele is forty-eight.

Last week when Lamar learned about his mother's diagnosis, he immediately shared the sad news with his fiancée. So perhaps Marta has panicked about marrying a man she assumes will be afflicted by Alzheimer's at an early age.

Lamar wonders if Marta is right to worry. Perhaps he is at extra risk for early Alzheimer's. Perhaps he should not have a family and perhaps he could become a terrible burden to any spouse. Is Marta right to reject him?

Genotype/phenotype complexity

Many genes interact with many physical and social environments to shape normal traits, but one gene misfiring is sometimes sufficient to produce disorder. This is the case with Alzheimer's disease – which we will get back to in a moment — but also with other medical conditions. An example is the rare dementing illness called Huntington's disease, which destroys the fatty lining of nerve cells leading to loss of coordinated movement, emotional instability, psychosis, and mental decline. Huntington's is a dominant disorder, meaning that only one disease-related allele at a single locus need be present for the disease to manifest itself.

A gene on Chromosome 4 is implicated in Huntington's. (The chromosomes are numbered in order of their relative length; 4 is a relatively big chromosome.) However, this disease does not result from a single mutation to this gene. Rather, many different alleles for the gene lead to the same problematic result. These alleles differ from each other in one important way: they have a different number of tandem repeats — multiple copies of the same base sequence (sometimes called "stutters").

Cystic fibrosis is another single-locus disease that results from a great many (some 650) allelic variations of a single gene. Unlike Huntington's, cystic fibrosis is a recessive disorder; it takes two disease-related alleles at that locus for the disease

One gene misfiring is sufficient to produce some medical disorders. Such genes are relatively easy to find, compared to the genes that contribute to complex disorders.

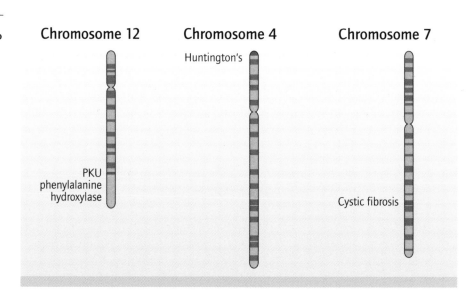

Chromosome 12

PKU
phenylalanine
hydroxylase

Chromosome 4

Huntington's

Chromosome 7

Cystic fibrosis

to emerge. Cystic fibrosis affects the mucus lining of the lungs, leading to breathing problems and other difficulties.

Some single-locus disorders follow a slightly different script: the allele or allelic pair contributing to disorder may occur in any of several different genes. As noted in Chapter 2, this is called genetic heterogeneity, and it is a characteristic of certain rare forms of breast and colon cancer as well as the early-onset form of Alzheimer's.

The important point is that single-gene disorders may result from one of many different alleles at one or more loci. Furthermore, any particular allele associated with a disorder may sometimes, but not always, lead to that disorder and may sometimes, but not always, lead to either a mild or severe form of the disorder.

The less-than-straightforward association between an allele and a disorder has to do with proteins. Recall that genes code for amino acids that combine into proteins that make up the structure of cells and direct their activities. A so-called "disease gene" has some alleles whose code results in a necessary protein and other alleles whose code does not have the necessary result. The gene "misfires" when the latter type of allele is present. This could mean that as a result of that allele's instructions, none of, not enough of, or too much of a resulting protein is produced. Or it could mean that the protein is not made properly and quickly becomes degraded.

The same unhappy results can occur when an allele is affected by modifier genes, that is, by alleles at other loci that interact with the allele in question.

Researchers theorize that the genotype/phenotype relationship may be threshold-dependent. Take, for example, a disorder that results when too little of a particular protein is produced. If protein quantities fall below a lower threshold, disorder will follow. When protein quantities rise above an upper threshold, no disorder will follow.

But when protein quantities lie between the two thresholds, disorder may or may not follow. There may be no symptoms, unnoticeable symptoms, mild symptoms, or serious symptoms. In other words, there is no predictable phenotype associated with that genotype. In such cases, whether or how the disorder manifests itself depends on environmental factors.

PKU is a disease that results when the body does not have enough of a particular enzyme; this enzyme is a protein that acts upon the liver. As described in Chapter 3, PKU can cause mental retardation. It also produces other effects, such as the lightening of hair and skin color.

The gene associated with PKU is called PAH (this stands for the enzyme involved, *phenylalanine hydroxylase*). More than 400 problematic alleles have been identified; according to one scientific report, the mutations include "deletions, insertions, missense mutations, splicing defects, and nonsense mutations."[1] Researchers had hoped that they could match up genotype with phenotype — that is, that based on the problem allele that is present, they could predict the symptoms and severity of the disease. If they could do this, then doctors could adjust treatment plans to each individual. Babies having alleles known to produce severe effects could be put on the highly restricted diet that prevents symptoms from appearing. Babies with alleles associated with milder effects could be put on less restrictive diets.

It has not turned out to be so simple. Many alleles are not consistently associated with any one PKU phenotype, that is, with any one set of symptoms. In the glum words of one research report, "Prognosis may not be predicted with precision based on mutation analysis."[2]

More genotype/phenotype complexity

PKU is a recessive disorder, like cystic fibrosis and unlike Huntington's, a dominant disorder. The disease occurs only in persons who inherit two problematic alleles of the same gene, one from each parent. Recessive and dominant disorders of this type illustrate Mendelian inheritance patterns. "Mendelian" refers to Gregor Mendel, a 19th century monk who raised pea plants and carefully recorded various traits that appeared in successive generations (color, shape, texture, size, etc.). Based on his experiments, Mendel proposed the theory that discrete units of heredity (what we now call genes) are passed from generation to generation in dominant and recessive patterns that can be calculated using simple mathematical formulas. All of modern genetics builds upon his original ideas.

Geneticists today realize that inheritance is more complicated than a simple Mendelian passing down of immutable genetic units. For example, with Huntington's disease, the allele that is passed down in dominant fashion through the generations alters slightly along the way. A sequence of DNA within the allele repeats itself (stutters) each time it gets passed down. When the string of repeats exceeds a certain length, the allele begins to malfunction — fails to properly instruct for the amino acids that will build a needed protein — and disease results. The age at onset of disease and

Based on his careful study of pea plants in the mid-1800s, Gregor Mendel proposed the idea that "discrete units of heredity" — what we now call the genes — are transmitted from one generation to the next in recessive and dominant patterns. Researchers now recognize that the inheritance patterns for many traits are more complicated.

they do not have a second X with a normal allele to compensate for the deficiency, the way that girls (XX) do.

The bottom line is that even for a single-locus disorder, inheriting a disease-related allele does not by itself foretell the presence of disease and the severity of symptoms. Once again, genotype may not always predict phenotype.

Fragile X syndrome can result in mild learning disabilities or more severe mental retardation. Resulting from a mutation in a single gene on the X chromosome, it occurs in 1 in 3,600 males and less often in females.

the speed of decline correlate positively with the number of stutters. Huntington's disease appears when there are more than 35 repeats but not when there are fewer than 35 repeats. Importantly, there are rare, unexplained exceptions.

Fragile X syndrome, the most commonly inherited form of mental retardation, is another disorder that occurs when a string of repeats in a gene lengthens. As with Huntington's, Fragile X appears when there is a high number of base repeats (above 200) in the relevant gene. There appears to be only a modest relationship between the number of repeats above 200 and the severity of the disease.

There's a second twist to the inheritance pattern of Fragile X. The disorder is what is known as an X-linked disorder or trait. A gene with the disease-causing alleles appears on the X chromosome that, along with its counterpart the Y chromosome, defines gender. Boys (XY) are more frequently and severely affected by Fragile X because if they have a problematic allele on their X chromosome,

Polygenic disorders: complexity multiplied

Some mental disorders have no conspicuous genetic component; the loss of memory that we call amnesia is typically caused by a hit to the head, not a genetic problem. And as we emphasized earlier, most genetic disorders do not result from alleles at a single locus. PKU, Huntington's, and Fragile X are exceptions to the rule.

The vast majority of mental disorders are believed to be polygenic: health problems occur when disease-related alleles are inherited for many different genes. Most mental disorders also are multifactorial, which means that multiple environmental and genetic factors are operating in an intricate, epigenetic fashion to upset the stable development and functioning of cells. (The adjective "complex" is often used in the same sense as "multifactorial.")

Earlier in this chapter, we pointed out that with most single-gene disorders, a disease-related allele sometimes, but not always, leads to the disorder and sometimes, but not always, leads to either a mild or severe form of the disorder. This qualifying statement applies to alleles involved in polygenic disorders, too. Each of the many potentially problematic alleles sometimes, but not always, contributes to triggering a disorder and sometimes, but not always, contributes to a mild or severe form of the disorder.

A polygenic disorder results only when all of the pertinent genetic and environmental factors are in place, and the extent of disorder depends on when those factors occur and how they affect each other. The difficulty of predicting phenotype from genotype is compounded exponentially.

Schizophrenia, a polygenic disorder

Schizophrenia is an example of a polygenic mental disorder with an ambiguous genotype-phenotype relationship. It is a common form of mental illness compared to PKU and Huntington's, affecting about 1 percent of the general population. About half of all cases manifest themselves in adolescence or early adulthood.

Schizophrenia stems from incoordination of brain function. It is as though circuits inside the brain get crossed. The brain loses its ability to process thoughts, words, and emotions as it normally would. Affected persons become confused, paranoid, and/or delusional. They may believe spies are following them or that aliens are beaming them messages. They can become apathetic and emotionally stunted, which causes them to isolate themselves from other people and to abandon cleanliness or other social norms. People affected by an episode of schizophrenia often make no sense to others and can be impossible to reason with. They often become social outcasts. Many of the homeless suffer from this disorder.

With some people the symptoms of schizophrenia appear gradually. With others the symptoms show up in a sudden, dramatic change of behavior. Some people experience schizophrenic symptoms only occasionally, while others are chronically affected. Like many chronic diseases, schizophrenia is not curable, though medicine and behavior therapy can often control some symptoms. In some cases — not predictably — improvement and virtually full recovery occur. Symptoms often decline with age.

For a long time schizophrenia was believed to be the result of faulty parenting, the victim's weak personality, or God's punishment. But beginning in the 1960s, researchers conducting family, twin, and adoption studies recognized that relatives of affected persons are much more likely to themselves become schizophrenic, compared to people in the general population. Indeed, there is a ten-fold increase in risk for persons who have siblings with the disease. This implies that schizophrenia has a familial, perhaps hereditary, component. That research did not lead to a cure for schizophrenia, but it did provide great relief to parents and patients who had previously shouldered the blame for the disease.

Molecular scientists have put a great deal of effort into finding the susceptibility genes for schizophrenia. A susceptibility gene is one for which certain alleles make you susceptible to — at higher risk for — a disorder, while other alleles make you less liable to have the disorder. A disorder will appear in those instances where a particular allele appears in conjunction with problematic alleles at other loci *plus* environmental triggers. ("Susceptibility" as an adjective also is used to describe genes that affect traits not associated with disorder, such as a "susceptibility gene" for musicality.)

Studies on schizophrenia have "implicated" various genes and chromosomal regions, but they have produced only tentative results that remain unconfirmed despite replication studies that have been attempted.[3] The failure to pin down schizophrenia susceptibility genes is frustrating, but it does not mean that such genes do not exist. Rather, it underscores the complexity of the disease. It serves as evidence that the disease is genetically heterogeneous: multiple genetic factors provide different pathways to the same disease.

It is important to note here that the vast majority of people who have first-degree relatives with schizophrenia do not end up with the disease themselves.

Something besides genes is at play, but it is not clear what that is. So another question is, what environmental factors interact with susceptibility genes to launch the onset of schizophrenia?

Researchers are exploring various causal theories. Viral infections that alter brain chemistry are suspected to play a role in some, but perhaps not all, instances of this disease. Head injuries are another possible factor, in some cases. So are prenatal infections such as rubella, developmental problems triggered by complications at birth, and drug abuse. In short, what we call schizophrenia may have many different causes and is probably several distinct diseases. The search for genetic components to schizophrenia is merely one track in the manifold investigations into this tragic and disabling form of mental disorder.

A significant percentage of the homeless in the U.S. today suffer from schizophrenia or some other mental disorder. It is not yet known which environmental factors interact with genetics to cause these mental disorders to emerge.

Persons with bipolar disorder suffer from extreme swings in mood. In the manic state, they may be highly creative but also erratic, over-energetic, and irresponsible. In the depressed state, they may be sad, disinterested, and even suicidal.

Bipolar disorder, also polygenic

Like schizophrenia, bipolar disorder is a polygenic mental disorder with no clear genotype-phenotype relationship. Bipolar, also known as manic-depressive illness, causes extreme swings in mood.

In a depressed state, an affected person is overwhelmingly sad, disinterested in life, indecisive in the extreme, and unable to sleep or, alternatively, unable to stay alert. The person may feel worthless and be filled with despair, leading to suicidal impulses. It is estimated that 15 percent to 20 percent of patients suffering from bipolar disorder kill themselves, even though many are on medication.

In the manic state of bipolar disorder, the same person is highly elated and may also be extremely talkative, distractable, hypersexual, irresponsibly extravagant financially, and unable or unwilling to sleep. The person may feel extremely self-important and be willing to take extraordinary and dangerous risks.

For the person with bipolar disorder, extreme moods alternate with periods of more stable emotions. The mood swings may occur months or weeks apart, or they may cycle rapidly. The frequency of these mood swings tends to increase over time.

About one in every 100 persons has severe bipolar, and another one in 100 has a milder form of the disease. It occurs equally often in men and women and has its onset primarily in adulthood, though researchers believe it may be underdiagnosed in adolescents. Bipolar disorder is treated with medication and counseling, but these treatments are not effective in all cases nor to the same degree. Each physician has to experiment with treatments until one is found that works.

From this description of bipolar disorder, it should be apparent that its phenotype varies in each affected person. This is because the pathway from cause to disease varies in each person. Systematic studies of families, twins, and adoptees show that the risk of having bipolar disorder is far higher for persons who have close relatives with the disorder, compared to members of the general population.

As has been the case for schizophrenia, finding the specific genes involved in bipolar disorder has proven to be difficult. A pair of scientists writing about this odyssey have referred to it as a "manic depressive history."[4] Researchers using linkage analysis have identified more than a dozen different chromosomal regions or genes with lod scores high enough to suggest they are relevant to bipolar disorder.

Later investigations (called replications) have produced lower lod scores for the same genes, suggesting that perhaps they are not so relevant after all. A recent meta-analysis of genome scan studies could find no statistical significance for any nominated site.[5] One reasonable conclusion is that no one gene has such a significant effect that it can be revealed through linkage analysis. Thus, the search continues both for susceptibility genes for mental disorders and also for better methods of finding them.

Research challenges

There are no recognized laboratory tests for schizophrenia or bipolar disorder to help a physician confirm or disconfirm a diagnosis. Researchers know less about the etiology of these disorders (the pathways from cause to effect) than they do about the etiology of non-psychological diseases such as the various forms of cancer and diabetes. The same relative scarcity of knowledge also holds for other mental disorders such as anxiety disorder, post-traumatic stress disorder, eating disorders, and phobias. The etiology of Alzheimer's is relatively better understood, but not well enough yet to provide for adequate treatments.

Genetic research will help fill in the blanks, and here's how. As each susceptibility gene of large or small effect is identified, lab techniques can be used to entice the gene to express itself and

Many studies have sought to identify the susceptibility genes for bipolar (the genes that play some role in the disease), but so far none has been confirmed. Finding them may be difficult if there are many genes, each of small effect.

reveal the amino acids for which it codes and the proteins that result. Through a variety of techniques, researchers can then figure out what the proteins do when they are functioning properly and what happens when they malfunction. Following this trail for each gene, researchers hope to put together a better picture of what happens inside the body to cause the paranoia of schizophrenia, the mood swings of bipolar disorder, and the memory loss of Alzheimer's. Researchers are also attempting to discover more about the mostly unknown factors that regulate variability in gene expression. With such knowledge could come medicines that substitute for proteins the body needs, but is not able to produce properly itself or produces insufficiently due to problems in genetic coding.

By finding the genes at work in Alzheimer's disease, scientists hope to obtain clues to the environmental factors that also play a role.

The environmental part of the story may be neglected through this approach, but that is mainly because researchers have not yet found a good way to isolate and study each contributing environmental factor the way a gene can be isolated and studied. The complex interplay that occurs between biological processes and environments also gets neglected, though it is argued that approaching mental disorders through individual genes — as piecemeal and artificial as that may be — is a pragmatic and doable way to get started on this difficult puzzle.

Lamar's dilemma

Despite the considerable effort being expended in behavioral genetic research, results so far offer little practical help to the patient who already has a mental disorder. Very little can be done for Adele, who already suffers from Alzheimer's, nor for Lamar, who worries that himself may someday be afflicted with this disease.

Alzheimer's affects about 4 million Americans. That number is growing because people are living longer and the disease appears late in life. The biggest risk factor for expression of the disease is aging. It is estimated that perhaps as many as 10 percent of all people age 65 and older have the disease and up to 50 percent of all people age 85 and older. People with relatives affected by Alzheimer's are at somewhat higher risk themselves for acquiring the disease.

The form of Alzheimer's that has a late onset is what afflicts former U.S. President Ronald Reagan. It is a complex disorder, with many genes contributing. One gene identified as a contributing factor sits on Chromosome 19 and is called *apoE* (for apolipoprotein class E). Although the details remain unclear, researchers believe that the protein associated with this gene repairs connections between cells in the brain. This suggests that the problems of Alzheimer's occur when these repairs are no longer made properly.

ApoE appears in three different alleles called *apoE2, apoE3,* and *apoE4.* People who inherit one copy of *apoE4* (about a quarter of the population) have about four times the risk of developing Alzheimer's compared to the general population. People who inherit two copies of *apoE4*, one from each parent (about 2 percent of the population) are at a ten-fold increase in risk. The risk declines for people with *apoE3* alleles, and it declines even more for people with *apoE2* alleles.

About 5 percent of Americans with Alzheimer's have the rare early-onset varieties that strike people before age 65. This is the form of the disease that has affected Lamar's mother, Adele. Three different loci have been implicated in early Alzheimer's, and they are located on Chromosomes 1, 14, and 21. It is a dominant, single-locus disorder, which means that just one copy of a disease-related

Former U.S. President Ronald Reagan is among the millions of Americans who suffer from Alzheimer's, the most common form of dementia.

allele at any one of these three loci is enough to trigger the disease.

A diagnosis of Alzheimer's, both late-onset and early-onset, rests on a variety of factors, such as tests of cognitive functioning and mood (to gauge symptoms), blood and urine tests (to rule out other health problems), and brain scans (to rule out strokes). As yet there is no cure for Alzheimer's, although there are drugs that can delay the problems for some people.

Lamar's mother, with early-onset Alzheimer's, has obviously inherited one of the alleles associated with the disease. Recall that each person has a pair of alleles for every gene and passes only one of them down to each child. Lamar may have inherited the problem allele from his mother, in which case he has inherited the disease, or he may have inherited a benign allele from her, in which case he will escape the early onset form of the disease. (He would still share the general population's risk for the late onset form.)

Lamar could get a genetic test to find out whether he has inherited an allele associated with early-onset Alzheimer's. If the test shows he is free from such alleles, perhaps his fiancée Marta will reconsider marriage and life will be back to usual.

On the other hand, if the test shows he has an early-onset Alzheimer's allele, then Lamar has brought upon himself fore-knowledge of a sorry fate. Because early-onset Alzheimer's is a single-gene, dominant disorder, Lamar will most likely succumb to the slow destruction of his mind. How would such information affect his life in the meantime? Probably not well, based on reports in the medical literature on people who have obtained this knowledge.

Lamar may or may not want to know what his future holds, but at least he can choose whether or not to find out. That choice is not available to people concerned about their risks for the predominant forms of Alzheimer's. Because those forms of the disease are polygenic, the presence of *apoE4* or any other allele associated with the disease would only indicate level of risks, not certain diagnosis. No professional medical society recommends screening for the *apoE4* allele.

But, as Lamar probably realizes, there is little to be gained from getting tested for any form of Alzheimer's so long as no cure is known and treatment is palliative at best. In fact, there is much to be risked. Suppose, for example, that Lamar's employer obtains access to his medical records and learns he has an early-onset Alzheimer allele. The employer could misunderstand the information and presume Lamar is already diseased. Lamar could find himself moved to a position of less responsibility, cut off from promotion. The employer might even be tempted to fire Lamar out of fears that insurance premiums will climb if Lamar stays. This would all be quite unfair for Lamar since he may have left twenty or more years of healthful living.

Lamar's fiancée, of course, did not even wait for a test before jumping to conclusions and abandoning him. So perhaps Lamar has been spared marriage to someone so flighty. There's little else positive to see about his situation. But who knows? Before the disease appears in Lamar — if it does — researchers may have found the cure. They may have discovered the environmental factors Lamar should avoid to delay onset of the disease. They may have figured out how to synthesize the proteins his body needs in order to compensate for those his body inadequately produces. They may even know how to repair or replace unwanted alleles through gene therapy.

Normal and abnormal traits

There are opposing ways to look at mental disorder. One view is that they are all-or-none states, like pregnancy or measles. The other view is that disorders represent the extreme end of a continuum ranging from healthy to unhealthy or, to put it in psychological terms, from the normal to the pathological. These competing possibilities lead to such questions as whether the sad or introverted person differs in kind or degree from the depressed person, whether or not someone with an exuberant personality is just a few shades away from being uncontrollably manic, and whether absentmindedness is a preliminary form of dementia.

If a disorder is on a continuum with "order," then the location of the dividing line becomes important. Otherwise, treatment for disorder could someday extend into treatment for normal conditions.

One way to distinguish mental disorder from normal mental functioning is to say that a disorder is one that has a detrimental effect on a person's ability to get along in society. But sometimes that's hard to say. Vincent Van Gogh suffered greatly from severe mental problems, yet he was one of the greatest artists of the 19th century. Many have pointed to a putative link between creative genius and mental disorder. Some researchers say that a feature common to both is greater emotional range. If this is the case, then the quest to eliminate mental disorder

Vincent Van Gogh suffered from mental disorder, possibly bipolar. This self-portrait reveals his indisputable talent, yet also hints at his internal disturbance. Some researchers believe that there may be a relationship between mental illness and creativity.

could have the unintended effect of eliminating positive traits as well. For a mental disorder such as Alzheimer's, it is hard to imagine what the related positive trait might be, but someday scientists may prove that it is simply the extreme opposite of some beneficial protein processes rather than a unique aberration.

Notes

1   National Institutes of Health (2000), p. 10.

2   See Enns *et al.* (1999). See Dipple (2000) which quotes Enns.

3   See for example Williams, H. J. *et al.* (2003), disconfirming the association between the PRODH gene on Chromosome 22 and schizophrenia. See also the vague conclusion of the abstract for a genome scan meta-analysis by Lewis, C. M. *et al.* (2003), p. 34: "The results suggest that some or all of [more than a dozen chromosomal] regions contain loci that increase susceptibility to schizophrenia in diverse populations."

4   See Risch, N. and D. Botstein (1996).

5   Segurado, R. *et al.* (2003).

RESOURCES FOR CHAPTER 5

ABC News. 2002. "Early onset Alzheimer's diagnosis, treatment, and challenges of this rare disorder." (Accessed 26 November); available at http://www.abcnews.go.com/sections/living/DailyNews/early_onsetAD020731.html.

Alzheimer's Association. 2002. "What is Alzheimer's disease?" (accessed 26 November); available at http:www.alz.org/AboutAD/WhatIsAD.htm.

---. 2002. "Ethical issues in Alzheimer's disease: Genetic testing." (Accessed 26 November); available at http: www.alz.org/ResourceCenter/FactSheets/FSGeneticTesting.pdf.

---. 2002. "Information sheets: genetics and Alzheimer's disease." (Accessed 26 November); available at http://www.alzheimers.org.uk/about/info_genetics.html.

Chakravarti, A. 2002. "A compelling genetic hypothesis for a complex disease: PRODH2/DGCR6 variation leads to schizophrenia susceptibility." *Proceedings of the National Academy of Sciences* 99: 4755-4756.

Childs, B., with the assistance of J. McInerney, for the Foundation for Genetic Education & Counseling. 2000. "A framework for genetics and complex disease." (Accessed 7 December); available at http://www.fgec.org/framework_for_complex_disease.htm

Dipple, K. M. and E. R. B. McCabe. 2002. "Phenotypes of patients with 'simple' mendelian disorders are complex traits: Thresholds, modifiers, and systems dynamics." *American Journal of Human Genetics* 66: 1729-1735.

Enns, G. M., D. R. Martinez, A. L. Kuzmin, R. Koch, C. K. Wakeem, S. L. C. Woo, R. C. Eisensmith, et al. 1999. "Molecular correlations in phenylketonuria: mutation patterns and corresponding biochemical and clinical phenotypes in a heterogenous California population." *Pediatric Research* 46: 594-602.

Foundation for Genetic Education & Counseling. 2000. "Genetics and bipolar disorder (manic depressive illness)." (Accessed 7 December); available at http://www.fgec.org/genetic&bipolar_disorder.htm.

Gottesman, I. I. 2002. "The ups and downs of genes and bipolar disorder." (unpublished; personal communication to The Hastings Center Behavior Genetics Working Group.)

Grody, W. 2001. "Determining risk for cystic fibrosis: Carrier patients may be the key." (Accessed 15 August); available at http://www.geneletter.com/08-15-01/features/cfcarrierrisk.html.

Health Canada in Co-operation with the Schizophrenia Society of Canada. 2002. "Schizophrenia: A handbook for families." (Accessed 7 September); available at http://www.hc-sc.gc.ca/hppb/mentalhealth/pubs/schizophrenia/

Lewis, C. M. et al. 2003. "Genome Scan Meta-Analysis of Schizophrenia and Bipolar Disorder, Part II: Schizophrenia." *American Journal of Human Genetics* 77: 34-48.

Liu H., G. R. Abecasis, S. C. Heath, A. Knowles, S. Demars, Y. J. Chen, J. L. Roos, J. L Rapoport , J. A. Gogos , and M. Karayiorgou. 2002. "Genetic variation in the 22q11 locus and susceptibility to schizophrenia." *Proceedings of the National Academy of Sciences* 99: 16859-64.

Maugh II, T. H. 1997. "Scientists find how gene leads to Huntington's." *Los Angeles Times* 8 August (Accessed 30 November); available at http://www.dhh-ev.de/alt/la080897/html.

Moldin, S. O., and I. I. Gottesman. 1997. "At issue: Genes, experience, and chance in schizophrenia." *Schizophrenia Bulletin*, National Institutes of Mental Health 23: 547-561.

National Institutes of Health. 2000. *NIH consensus statement: Phenylketonuria (PKU): Screening and management.* 17, No. 3.

Nuffield Council on Bioethics. 1998. *Mental disorders and genetics: The ethical context.* London: Nuffield Council on Bioethics.

Nuffield Council on Bioethics. 2002. *Genetics and human behaviour.* London: Nuffield Council on Bioethics.

Risch, N., and D. Botstein. 1996. "A manic depressive history." *Nature Genetics* 12: 351-353.

Segurado, R. 2003. "Genome Scan Meta-Analysis of Schizophrenia and Bipolar Disorder, Part III: Bipolar Disorder." *American Journal of Human Genetics* 73: 49-62.

"Stanford researchers establish link between creative genius and mental illness." 2002 (accessed 2 December); available at http://www.talentdevelop.com/StanfordResearchers.html.

Williams H. J., N. Williams, G. Spurlock, N. Norton, S. Zammit, G. Kirov, M. J. Owen, M. C. O' Donovan. 2003. "Detailed analysis of PRODH and PsPRODH reveals no association with schizophrenia." *American Journal of Medical Genetics* 120B(1): 42-6.

HOW IS THE ABILITY TO CONTROL IMPULSES AFFECTED BY GENES AND ENVIRONMENTS?

6

■ ■ ■ Trevor, in trouble with the law

Growing up on a farm in Iowa, Trevor was always into some crazy adventure — leaping out of barn windows, diving off high rock into the quarry pond, or racing his four-wheeler across unplowed fields. His parents doted on him and let him do as he pleased.

He was a restless youth who never stuck with any activity for long, until he discovered cars. There were several junkers on the farm and he learned from his father how to fix their engines and bodies. When he was sixteen, Trevor put together a stockcar from old parts and smashed his way to a blue ribbon at the state fair's demolition derby.

Trevor dropped out of high school in the twelfth grade and into his early thirties travelled the country on the stock car racing circuit. In this high-risk sport, he was notable for the risks he was willing to take. This is attested to by his many injuries and his many wrecked cars. Trevor's reckless attitude — plus the heavy drinking and gambling that got him into a variety of trouble — eventually forced him out of racing.

With huge debts, Trevor got a job in a warehouse in Oklahoma. One day he impulsively stole some goods from the warehouse and fenced them. It was so easy that he began to regularly support his income in this fashion. One night with a lot of cash in his hands and investigators on his tail, Trevor decided to skip town. He and his girlfriend sped off in his souped-up sports car, but they didn't get far. The car flipped going 130 miles an hour down a Texas highway. Today Trevor is in jail, charged with manslaughter in the death of his girlfriend.

Trevor's family hired him a lawyer who, while doing some library research, learned about a couple of instances where defendants have pleaded not guilty by reason of their genetics. The lawyer wonders if he might be able to pursue this kind of defense. Could Trevor plausibly plead not guilty based on the argument that he was genetically compelled to act rashly?

It's normal behavior to shout, wave your arms, and jump out of your seat at a sports arena. A child who behaves that way too often in school might be suspected of having ADHD.

Impulsive behavior and ADHD

There is a saying that a weed is merely a plant out of place. The same could be said of many character traits. The boisterous person might be out of place in a monastery dedicated to silence but not in the stands at a basketball game. Boisterousness, its counterpoint meekness, and many other aspects of personality are undesirable traits only when they create problems for the person displaying them or for others who interact with that person.

Are some character traits always and in every circumstance undesirable? This interesting question has been raised in the context of attention-deficit hyperactivity disorder (ADHD), a controversial but increasingly frequent diagnosis of children with problem behavior.

The primary traits associated with ADHD are impulsive activities and short attention spans. Both traits are universal to all children; however, they become hallmarks of ADHD when a child exhibits them to a much larger degree than other children of the same age in similar settings.

ADHD symptoms usually appear when children reach the ages of three to five, though in many cases they are not noticed until later. Up to 10 percent of all schoolchildren worldwide have ADHD, according to some estimates; this disorder has been found in every nation and culture where researchers have looked for it. It affects a much larger proportion of boys than girls. The problems associated with ADHD can persist into adulthood, affecting work performance and personal relationships.

Scientists speculate that ADHD is caused by underdevelopment of several parts of the brain critical to such mental tasks as being aware of oneself and time; resisting distractions; over-riding immediate impulses with reasoned responses; and delaying gratification. One way ADHD has been described is that affected persons display too much public speech and behavior; they have not learned how to internalize and self-correct their thoughts and actions.

A variety of unproven environmental factors have been suspected of triggering ADHD. These include premature birth, maternal alcohol and tobacco use, exposure to high levels of lead in early childhood, inoculations, infections, and brain injuries. Researchers have pretty much ruled out diet and child-rearing methods as causal factors for ADHD.

Researchers estimate that ADHD is 70 to 80 percent heritable. This refers to the variation in the incidence of ADHD in a population that can be attributed to genetic factors. Heritability estimates do not tell us what to expect for individuals, but family studies tell us that a child is much more likely to be diagnosed with ADHD if a sibling or parent has been diagnosed.

ADHD is believed to be polygenic, involving several genes that are normally very active in the parts of the brain that appear underdeveloped in persons suffering from ADHD.

Much research attention has focused on genes involved in the regulation of dopamine. This is a neurotransmitter, a brain chemical that carries messages between nerve cells. Some genes code for dopamine to be taken up by "receptor" nerve cells, other genes code for dopamine to be distributed by "transporter" nerve cells, and still other genes code for unused dopamine to be reabsorbed by transporter nerve cells for re-use later.

Various genes related to these functions have been tentatively associated with ADHD. One such candidate is called SNAP-25, located on Chromosome 20. In a study published in 2002, genome scans were conducted on 93 Irish families that had two or more members with ADHD. According to that study's results, one particular allele for the SNAP-25 gene is 50 percent more likely to appear in persons with ADHD than in persons without it. Other studies have found small associations with other

Fewer girls than boys are diagnosed with ADHD, but the total number of children diagnosed is large and climbing. According to some estimates, up to 10 percent of all schoolchildren worldwide have the disorder.

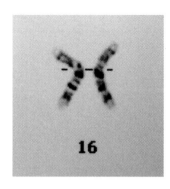

Based on results of genome scans, some researchers propose that a gene associated with ADHD resides on Chromosome 16. Using similar studies, other research has led to the suggestion that a gene associated with autism may lie on the same region of the chromosome. This has led some researchers to wonder whether the same gene is involved in both disorders.

alleles for SNAP-25.[1]

Another study published in 2002 suggests that a gene associated with ADHD may lie somewhere within a specific region of Chromosome 16. This study also included genome scans, conducted on 203 families with more than one child diagnosed with ADHD. The scans revealed a series of molecular markers (DNA sequences that vary from human to human) on Chromosome 16 shared by sibling pairs more than 50 percent of the time. Since siblings share on average 50 percent of their alleles, this higher rate of sharing for the molecular markers may correlate with the occurrence of ADHD.[2]

Interestingly, other genome scan studies suggest that this region on Chromosome 16 may also include a gene associated with autism. This is a complex developmental disability that emerges in early childhood and interferes with the normal development of social skills and communication. Since about 150 genes lie within this region of Chromosome 16, it may not be the same gene associated with both ADHD and autism. But researchers speculate that if it is the same gene, then perhaps one neurobiological mechanism – one process involving cells of the brain — underlies both disorders.

It must be remembered that the claims for ADHD susceptibility genes at SNAP-25, the region on Chromosome 16, and several other locations remain unconfirmed. They are based on small, preliminary studies that need replication.

The ultimate quest is not to find the *one* gene that causes this disorder; rather, it is to find the many genes and the many environmental factors that operate interactively to trigger the range of behaviors clustered under the ADHD diagnosis.

Is ADHD a disorder or a trait?

There has been an epidemic of ADHD diagnoses in recent years. In 1985, the U.S. had between 650,000 and 750,000 individuals diagnosed with ADHD. By the year 2000 this number exceeded 4 million. School-age children receive the bulk of ADHD diagnoses, and more than three-quarters of those diagnosed are prescribed drugs (stimulants and/or anti-depressants) that serve to slow down brain activity.

Critics of the skyrocketing rate of diagnoses suggest that many children labelled ADHD may actually be suffering from allergies or may be acting out of frustration caused by undiagnosed visual problems or learning disabilities. Other critics point out that in the past people took a more benign view of the behaviors now associated with ADHD; rambunctiousness used to be considered in the range of normal. Some even theorize that the traits associated with ADHD were favorable adaptations in early humans because it took quick reaction times to succeed as hunters.

It also has been argued that increases in cases of ADHD are occurring not because there has been an increase in brain dysfunction among children, but rather because an ADHD diagnosis is highly subjective, convenient, and acceptable. The diagnosis is based in part (sometimes in whole) on observations from people such as teachers who do not have medical training; it opens the door for special services from education systems; ADHD medication makes children more docile and less challenging; and the public now has a very relaxed attitude about treating problems with drugs.

It also has been pointed out that if children today are more restless and distractable, it is not because of problems inside their heads but rather because of problems in our culture. The fast pace of life, the onslaught of media messages, consumerist clutter, reduced opportunities for children to run free and play actively, fewer chores and other responsibilities given to children that would teach them to behave maturely: these are the conditions of modern life that create restless and out-of-control children, they say.

Others argue that restlessness and distractibility are natural to children; what is unnatural is our restrictive social environments. As one commentator has pointed out, "Why don't we have a disorder called 'quiet listening'? Maybe 'bodily shrieking' is the healthier behavior."[3] The controversy over whether ADHD is a medical or social disorder complicates but does not impede the search for the underlying genetic contributors to the behavior.

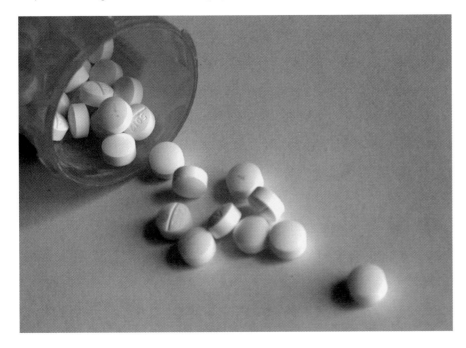

The majority of children diagnosed with ADHD are prescribed drugs to modify their behavior.

Novelty seeking – the drive to experience new and stimulating experiences – is a form of impulsive behavior that tends to result in positive consequences for the individual or society.

Novelty-seeking: a positive impulsive trait

Impulsivity, a prominent feature in ADHD, is also a feature of a behavior with more positive social connotations. This behavior is called novelty seeking, and it has been a favorite subject of study for genetic researchers. Novelty seekers are people who thrive on new experiences and heightened sensations. They enjoy adventures such as skydiving, mountain climbing, travel to exotic locations, or other extreme experiences.

Researchers identify novelty seekers through personality inventories completed by subjects about themselves and through scores on rating scales completed by observers of individuals. Those who score high in the trait are described as "impulsive, exploratory, and extravagant," while those who score low are described as "stolid" or "reflective and rigid."

Researchers speculate that novelty seeking, like ADHD, is related to activity of the brain chemical dopamine. In 1996, two association studies found a tentative correlation between novelty seeking and particular alleles of a gene called DRD4.[4] Some subsequent studies supported a correlation between longer DRD4 alleles (i.e., those with more tandem repeats) and the novelty-seeking trait, while others contradicted it. A 2002 meta-analysis of DRD4 studies could not find any statistical association. The authors of this meta-analysis study suggested that

the correlation may occur in the presence of as-yet-unknown "moderating" genes, which would account for contradictory findings.[5] Still more studies have explored but not confirmed a connection between DRD4 alleles and alcoholism, drug abuse, depression, and ADHD.

Antisocial personality: a negative impulsive trait

Impulsivity is central to a slew of disorders listed in the key clinical reference book known as DSM-IV-TR.[6] Along with ADHD, these include intermittent explosive disorder (the loss of control over impulses toward aggression), kleptomania (the impulse to steal unneeded objects), pyromania (the impulse to set objects on fire), trichotillomania (the impulse to pull out one's own hair), and other disorders.

Yet another diagnosis in DSM-IV-TR is antisocial personality disorder. A broad range of conduct falls under the label antisocial personality disorder and includes lying, cheating, breaking the law, aggressiveness, lack of social conscience, violating social norms, and acting with reckless disregard for others. It is the same condition that used to be described as "psychopathic" and "sociopathic."

Researchers theorize that antisocial personality disorder may emerge when persons with predisposing genotypes experience stressful environments. Specific genes remain wholly unidentified, but correlations have been found for

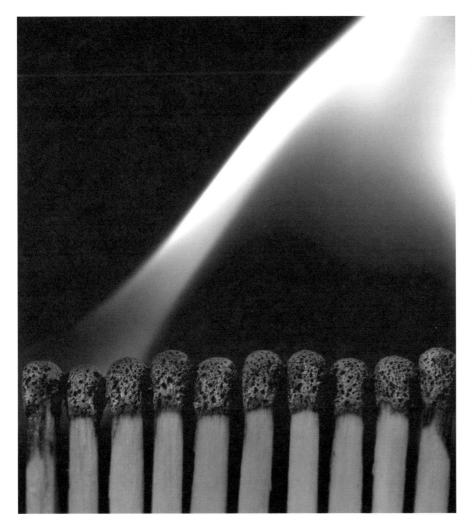

Pyromania — the obsessive desire to set objects on fire — is a form of impulsive behavior that tends to result in negative consequences for the individual and society.

such environmental factors as living in a poor urban area, living in high-density housing, experiencing violence in the home, and living with other familial dysfunctions.

One relevant study, of two-year-old twins in England and Wales, indicates that living in a deprived neighborhood is a greater risk factor for emotional and behavioral problems than any genetic factor.[7] Many people grow up in deprived neighborhoods yet do not become antisocial. This is evidence that a given environment does not by itself cause antisocial personality disorder. By the same token, there is little likelihood that any particular gene causes antisocial behavior by itself.

In 2001, a meta-analysis was conducted of 51 twin and adoption studies having to do with antisocial behavior. Through this project, scientists found that these proportions best explain the variance of antisocial behavior in the general population: additive genetic influence, .32; nonadditive genetic influence, .09; shared environment, .16; and nonshared environment, .43.[8] Think of these numbers as percentages. Note that they do not explain *how* genetic and environmental factors operate to affect the trait. They merely indicate that different genetic and environmental factors are present and exerting influence to relative degrees.

Many studies suggest that antisocial behavior peaking in adolescence (so-called juvenile delinquency) is more heavily influenced by the environment, specifically, peer pressure. In comparison, antisocial behavior that shows up in early childhood and continues throughout life may be more heavily influenced by genes.

Criminality: a legal description, not a trait

Antisocial personality disorder may propel an individual into crime but not everyone who commits a crime is antisocial. Nor are all crimes committed impulsively. A case in point is the civil rights activist of the 1960s who deliberately violated the law to protest Whites-only lunch counters. Criminality is not an official diagnosis in DSM-IV-TR; rather, it is a popular label for breaking the law, being arrested, or being convicted of a crime.

Criminality has been a target of study in behavioral genetics for two major and distinct reasons. First, crime is an issue of significant public concern. Second, the official records from the criminal justice system are an abundant source of data.

Yet research into criminality is problematic because, as many sociologists have pointed out, criminality is not an objectively measurable trait such as blood pressure or height. Rather, it is a social construct. There probably is not any behavior that is criminal across all contexts. Child sacrifice was acceptable in ancient Carthage, but in modern societies infanticide is a repugnant criminal act. In Industrial Age England, a poor wretch in the city could be put to death for stealing linen scraps from a factory, but a member of the gentry did not face penalties for enclosing commons land. Until 2003 in the United States, it was a crime (in some states but not in others) to engage in consensual homosexual sex in

The genetic and environmental factors underlying juvenile delinquency may differ in combination from those underlying lifelong criminal behavior.

It is a crime to possess small amounts of marijuana in the United States but it is not a crime in Canada. Such disparities make it quite difficult for researchers investigating the genetic basis of "criminality" to objectively define the trait.

the privacy of one's home. Today it is against the law to possess small amounts of marijuana in the United States, but it is not a crime in neighboring Canada.

Furthermore, enforcement of the law is selective. Traffic cops are much more likely to pull over Black or Latino drivers than White drivers. Blacks and Latinos also are much more likely to be pursued on drug charges than Whites, even though the latter violate drug laws in far greater numbers. The criminal defendant who can afford private attorneys stands a better chance of avoiding conviction than the defendant who must rely on court-appointed lawyers.

In sum, cultural variables determine which deeds and which persons are labelled criminal. "Criminality" *per se* is not an intrinsic trait, and this is important to keep in mind when reading about genetic research in this area.

Research into criminality

A highly publicized study of criminality was published in 1965. Chromosomal analysis of 197 men in a Scottish high-security prison found that seven of them had an extra Y chromosome. (The standard pattern is for women to have two X chromosomes and for men to have one X and one Y). The 7/197 ratio at the Scottish hospital led the researchers to suggest that an extra Y chromosome might cause aggressive behavior and mental "subnormality."[9]

Later studies showed that XYY men were taller, lower in intelligence, at greater risk for severe acne, and more likely to be imprisoned, on average, than XY men. However, these studies did not support the association between XYY and aggressive behavior. It also was discovered that XYY men are relatively common: about 1 in every 1,000.

The XYY chromosome has been found in many men leading normal, law-abiding lives. One plausible theory is that XYY men may be more likely to end up in jail because their lower average intelligence depresses their ability to find gainful work and to make wise choices.

While the XYY/crime connection is indirect at best, another chromosome combination is strongly linked to criminal behavior. Geneticists like to point out with a smile that if you have a single Y chromosome you are much more likely to commit a criminal offense than if you do not have one. Indeed, males make up a much larger proportion of the prison population than females.

Much of more recent research into the genetics of criminality has focused on an enzyme in the brain called MAO (monoamine oxidase). MAO's job is to break down excess neurotransmitters. Insufficient amounts of MAO can lead to the accumulation of neurotransmitters and this can interfere with the proper relay of messages between nerve cells and between nerve cells and muscles.

Low levels of MAO are correlated with mental retardation. They also are correlated with the behavior problems of addiction, reduced inhibition, lack of self-control, and aggression. Several studies have found a relationship between low MAO levels and criminality. This has led to a theory that people who have low MAO levels react more impulsively to circumstances and are therefore more likely to commit a crime.

In the 1980s, a Dutch family came to the attention of researchers. The reason was that, over several generations, male members of this family had been prone to violent and aggressive outbursts. These men had committed various criminal acts such as raping a sister, stabbing a man with a pitchfork, committing arson, and attempting to run over another man with a car.

In the early 1990s, researchers began focusing on a gene on the X chromosome that coded for a version of the MAO enzyme called MAOA. They discovered that the aggressive males in the Dutch family shared a particular allele for this gene. However, this notorious allele appears to be confined to the Dutch family. Criminals outside the family have different alleles, some leading to low MAOA levels and others not.[10]

MAOA came up again in a 2002 study of 500 males. It was found that the men with genotypes leading to low levels of MAOA were significantly more likely to be antisocial as adults, but only if they had been maltreated and abused as children. The men with genotypes leading to low levels of MAOA who had not been maltreated did not become antisocial, nor did those men with genotypes leading to high levels of MAOA who were maltreated. The study is significant because it demonstrates the critical role of gene-environment interaction.[11]

The myth of "genes for criminality"

When the Scottish XYY research was first published, news accounts unfortunately tended toward the sensational. Many members of the public came to the frightening conclusion that this chromosomal combination creates Frankenstein-like supermales. In similar fashion, press coverage of research on the Dutch family's unusual MAOA allele tended to exaggerate findings, leading many to believe that a "gene for criminality" had been discovered.

In the words of a pair of scientists writing on this topic, "Notions such as 'genes for crime' are nonsense." They add:

> … the following kind of notion is reasonable: There may be partially genetically influenced predispositions for certain behavioral tendencies, such as impulsivity, that in certain experiential contexts, make the probability of committing certain kinds of crimes higher than for individuals who possess lesser degrees of such behavioral tendencies.[12]

Note the phrase "certain experiential contexts." Given one set of unfolding circumstances, a particular genotype might tip a person toward socially approved behaviors. Given another set of circumstances, that same genotype might tip the person toward socially unacceptable behaviors. Imagine a person who storms into a house on fire to rescue victims trapped inside. Now imagine another

There is a genetic difference between men and women: most men have one X and one Y chromosome, and most women have two X chromosomes. There also is a difference in the incarceration rates of men and women: the percentage of men in prison is much higher than the percentage of women. Researchers are interested in understanding the correlation between these two facts.

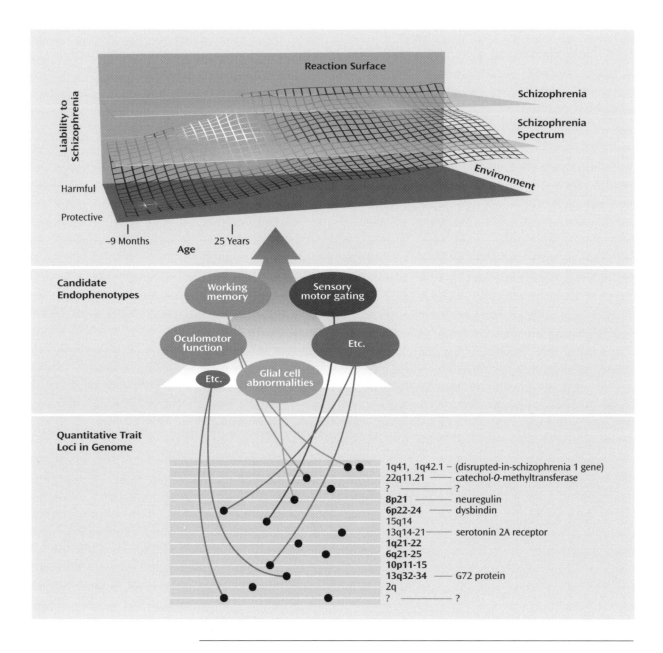

Reaction Surface

Liability to Schizophrenia

Schizophrenia

Schizophrenia Spectrum

Environment

Harmful

Protective

−9 Months   25 Years

Age

Candidate Endophenotypes

Working memory

Sensory motor gating

Oculomotor function

Etc.

Etc.

Glial cell abnormalities

Quantitative Trait Loci in Genome

1q41, 1q42.1 – (disrupted-in-schizophrenia 1 gene)
22q11.21 —— catechol-O-methyltransferase
? ———— ?
8p21 ———— neuregulin
6p22-24 —— dysbindin
15q14
13q14-21—— serotonin 2A receptor
1q21-22
6q21-25
10p11-15
13q32-34 —— G72 protein
2q
? ———— ?

Many genes, both known and unknown, contribute to the traits that together characterize the illness known as schizophrenia. The trampoline-like "reaction surface" illustrates the range of possible phenotypes given genetic and environmental inputs over a lifetime.

Illustration © Irving I. Gottesman. Used with permission.

person who storms into a locked home to burgle it. It is not hard to further imagine one person who could do both deeds in response to different stimuli.

Geneticists describe this collection of possible outcomes as a norm of reaction or reaction range. These terms describe the variety of phenotypes that result from a given genotype across each possible environment. It is visually depicted as a trampoline-like surface that dips up or down depending on the pressure of various genetic and environmental inputs.

It is possible today to sketch the norm of reaction for a plant, as we know from the study with yarrow cited in Chapter 3 and scores of similar botanical experiments. Plants can be grown in conditions that each vary by only one factor such as a gene or a degree of sun, soil, light, or nutrient. It is not yet possible to sketch the norm of reaction for a human behavior. Humans cannot be constrained and bred the way plants can. Their genetic makeup and their environments vary to far greater degrees. Behavior is far more difficult to define and measure than plant heights or flower petal numbers.

Add in developmental interactions that occur in a human life and the elements that must be included in a norm of reaction become infinite. However, it may eventually become possible to sketch the norm of reaction for the most significant environmental and genetic factors that operate together to influence a person's behavior.

Trevor's defense

Based on available evidence from the field of behavioral genetics, one can state emphatically that genes do not equal fate. The lawyer's legal scheme for Trevor dashes against this rock. A defense to the manslaughter charge based on genetics would very probably fail to acquit Trevor. It might even backfire.

When Trevor drove his car at very high speed, leading it to flip and fatally injure his passenger, he was acting impetuously and without regard to the possible consequences. Given his history of reckless behavior, he might try the "I couldn't help myself" defense. However, the criminal law tends to presume that free will prevails in most circumstances, so this is not an argument that judges or juries typically accept. Adding a genetic explanation to this excuse is not likely to improve Trevor's prospects.

Some defendants have tried to argue that they were not in charge of their behavior when they committed their crimes because they were intoxicated or under medication. These excuses rarely work, because one can choose to drink and one can choose to restrict one's own behavior while under medication (for example, by choosing not to drive while medicated). Sometimes these kind of mitigating factors lead to reduced charges or reductions in punishment, but they rarely allow the defendant to completely evade the legal consequences. For Trevor to argue that he could not help driving

A person on trial for death or injury from reckless driving might try to argue that "my genes made me do it!" However, that excuse probably will not work, because it is not scientifically based. Plus, the legal system presumes personal responsibility.

too fast because he was under the influence of his genes is therefore not likely to help him too much. Courts operate on the assumption that people must take responsibility for what they do regardless of underlying biological processes.

The main exception is insanity. In 1982, John Hinckley successfully used an insanity defense in court to escape conviction for his attempted assassination of President Ronald Reagan. The public was outraged. As a result, the insanity plea is much harder to win today. But many defendants avoid insanity pleas for another reason. The saying "out of the fire, into the frying pan" applies here: with an insanity plea you might avoid prison, but you'll end up instead in a hospital for the mentally ill where your sentence may be indefinite.

Another problem for Trevor is that even if he has a genetic excuse, he lacks an environmental excuse to go with it. Say, for example, that Trevor can claim to have a genotype that leads to low levels of

MAOA. A study cited earlier in this chapter suggests that adult antisocial behavior is more likely only if you have this MAOA profile and were abused as a child. Trevor cannot honestly claim to have been abused (though his lawyer might try this argument). In any event, reckless driving does not fall squarely into the category of antisocial behavior. At present, research provides Trevor with no other plausible genetic-environmental explanation for his behavior.

Legal scholars note that people are more likely to be excused for a crime if the conditions that caused them to commit the crime are relatively rare, not violent, not likely to be repeated, and treatable. Unfortunately for Trevor, these conditions do not hold with a genetics-based defense. First, large numbers of people carry low MAOA genotypes, the DRD4 allele, and other DNA markers and genes that have been associated, albeit tenuously, with various manifestations of impulsivity. If Trevor has one or more such alleles, it would not be rare. Second, Trevor's action resulted in a violent death. Third, if Trevor is not punished for his reckless driving it is reasonable to assume he will drive that way again. Fourth, it would be a real stretch to argue that medications available for impulsive disorders, such as the drug Ritalin for ADHD, guarantee a lighter foot on the gas pedal.

Legal scholars also speculate that bringing behavioral genetics into criminal cases will have less impact on trials than it will on case decisions made by prosecutors and judges. If Trevor claims "my genes made me do it," he may be sending the message that he cannot be reformed. This could motivate the prosecutor in criminal court to try the case instead of dropping it or plea bargaining (dropping serious charges if Trevor pleads guilty to a lesser charge). It also could impel the judge to give Trevor a harsher sentence once convicted.

Potential research consequences

Trevor may not be able to make use of genetics for his legal defense, but scientists may be able to make use of Trevor for behavioral genetic research. If he is convicted of manslaughter, information from his DNA will be entered into a database of convicted felons. Trevor's genotype will be profiled at more than a dozen loci where the number of tandem repeats varies. As of 2003, every U.S. state except Mississippi and Rhode Island had such a database networked into the FBI's CODIS (Combined DNA Index System), profiling more than 1.4 million offenders. The trend is for states to expand their DNA collections to include not only convicted felons, but also people convicted of misdemeanors as well as arrested suspects. It also has been proposed that the U.S. Justice Department establish a DNA database containing samples of anyone suspected of associating with terrorism.

Existing databases are proving to be highly useful tools by which law enforcers catch repeat offenders. DNA from a crime scene is compared to DNA in the databases. If a match occurs, this is evidence that is considered scientifically reliable and that is admissible by the courts.

Under current law, the tissue samples from which DNA is profiled (such as blood or saliva) are off limits to researchers, but they are tempting treasure troves and the law is subject to change. A major concern over opening sample collections to research is that they are not reflective of the population at large. For a variety of complex factors, the population of those arrested and convicted is disproportionately male, minority, and poor.

The possibility exists that a researcher conducting genome scans on samples collected for a criminal database might find an allele that occurs more than randomly and claim (or be misreported in the media as claiming) to have found a "gene for" criminal behavior. What the researcher might actually have found is an allele that is more common among, say, poor whites from the Bayou who couldn't afford good lawyers, Mexicans caught up by immigration violations, or African Americans who faced racist juries. Such a claim could lead to discriminatory actions against others of the same demographic group who share the allele.

Another consequence of genetic research that relies on arrest or conviction

As a piece of evidence leading from crime to criminal, DNA is surpassing fingerprints in importance. Samples of blood, skin cells, or hair left behind at the crime can be DNA-typed and compared to samples taken from suspects or checked against a database of samples from criminal offenders.

as synonyms for the criminal phenotype is that it will disproportionately focus on those who have committed "blue collar" crimes (assaults, property theft, petty drug offenses, etc.) compared to subjects who have committed "white collar" crimes (tax evasion, information theft, large-scale drug dealing, etc.). This is because those committing the latter type of crime are caught less often. Such research would inevitably reinforce the stereotype that the working class is more deviant than the professional class.

Treatment concerns

Genetic research into impulsivity will have substantial social value if the concerns described above can be overcome and if the research leads to treatment that prevents people from killing, stealing, and hurting others. The most likely form of treatment to come out of this research is medicines that compensate for improper levels of proteins and other compounds (such as electrolytes) that result from problem alleles. In the near future we can expect to see a wide range of behavior-moderating medicines developed as a direct result of gene research.

Another possible form of treatment is environmental intervention. We already know about some of the key non-genetic factors that promote healthy development and, as one part of that, good self-control: prenatal care, adequate nutrition, reduced exposure to toxins, improved education and work opportunities, and so forth. Behavioral genetic research may help us understand how specific environmental stimuli interact with specific genomes. This information could be used to try to prevent an individual's environment from undermining genetic mechanisms related to self-control.

In theory, gene therapy could someday be used to treat problem behavior. But so far gene therapy experiments to cure single-gene disorders have met with limited success. This means that gene therapy to treat polygenic behavior traits remains a very remote prospect.

Another medical intervention that could theoretically be used to avoid unwanted behavior is pre-implantation diagnosis and selection. In couples that have a family history of a single-gene disorder, the DNA of embryos created through in vitro fertilization can be analyzed for one or more disorders and/or traits; those without problem alleles can be selected for implantation into the mother. The procedure also is increasingly being used to select for gender. Given the complex and indirect relationship between genes and behavior, it is doubtful that this procedure could ever be used to select for behavior in any but the most approximate senses.

Past efforts to curb undesirable behavior through medical intervention give rise to fears about genetics-based efforts of the same kind. The history of the surgical procedure lobotomy is rele-

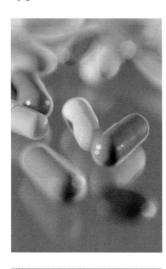

The scope and range of medicines used to treat antisocial behavior is likely to increase significantly as researchers learn more about the protein processes affected by genes.

vant here. A lobotomy is a slice into the brain. This reduces transmission of nerve messages between parts of the brain, which subdues behavior drastically and permanently.

In the late 1930s, the lobotomy came into vogue as a way to treat seriously mentally ill patients. This happened primarily through the promotional efforts of a single highly enthusiastic neurologist. The target population for the surgery soon expanded to include prison inmates, problem children, difficult family members, and political troublemakers. Tens of thousands of lobotomies were performed in the U.S. and around the world. In 1949, the surgeon who first developed a lobotomy procedure for use on humans was awarded the Nobel Prize in medicine. This gave a huge boost to the procedure's respectability and popularized it even more. But within a few years lobotomies fell out of favor due to the many ethical objections, the growing awareness of the operation's terrible side-effects, and the lack of evidence that the procedure worked. Also, by this time new drugs had emerged for treating uncontrollable behavior. The temporary ascendancy of this misguided treatment shows what can happen when the medical profession and the public jump too quickly on the bandwagon of unsubstantiated research.

The story of ADHD treatment is less dramatic, but equally pertinent to any discussion about medical treatment of behavior. Earlier in this chapter we

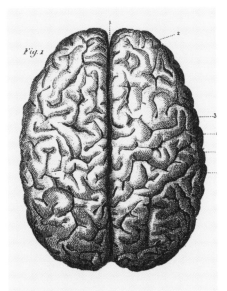

Fig. 1

The surgical procedure on the brain known as lobotomy was performed on tens of thousands of people in the twentieth century as a treatment for disruptive behavior. This occurred despite a lack of scientific evidence as to its effectiveness and serious ethical questions about its implementation. Some people worry that, in a similar fashion, gene-based medicines might gain popularity before the questions of effectiveness and ethics have been fully considered.

described the dramatic rise in the number of ADHD diagnoses in recent decades and the equally dramatic rise in the number of children being prescribed drugs for this condition. Many ADHD patients say — and their parents, doctors, and educators report — that with medication they are better able to focus and concentrate and less likely to act out inappropriately. These behavior changes allow them to do better in school, develop more friendships, and otherwise function like their non-ADHD peers.

On the other hand, some children exhibit side effects from these drugs such as nervousness, insomnia, depression, respiratory problems, blood pressure abnormalities, and cardiac complications. Research has yet to prove whether ADHD medications are safe for long-term use, especially with children who are still growing.

There are non-medical treatments for ADHD and these include placing affected children in smaller groups and more structured environments; teaching caregivers the strategies that work best for dealing with children who have a hard time staying focused; and providing children with behavior modification therapies. These treatments are time-consuming, more expensive in the short run, and more difficult to evaluate, which explains why they get short shrift compared to pharmacological solutions.

The moral of the story is that medication can easily become the first response to any perceived social problem. Genetic research could well increase the number of drugs used to treat behaviors. This gives renewed urgency to such questions as:

- What standards will be used to decide when a behavior is normal or in need of treatment?
- How do we select among different ways to treat the behavior?
- Who will have access to a behavior-moderating treatment that improves quality of life?
- What rights does a person have to refuse behavior-moderating treatment?
- Will our increased ability to control behavior reduce ranges of behaviors tolerated by society?
- What are the societal consequences when the range of acceptable behavior is restricted?

Other research concerns

Research into impulsive behavior, especially criminality, has been a flashpoint for controversy into behavioral genetic research in general. Many people believe that scientific facts often get highjacked (and pseudo-facts invented) to reinforce existing stereotypes and injustices. By this line of reasoning, any research into the genetics of criminality will do more harm than good.

Some people complain that because science is so revered in our culture, genetic explanations for behavior get more respect than other explanations. Sociologists raise an interesting point in this context. They note that the vast majority of variation in human behavior is cultural, not genetic. The clothing people

Genetic research will increase the number of medications available to treat children with ADHD. Yet some people question whether prescribing drugs is the most effective or appropriate response to children's behavior problems.

The Western rancher wears a cowboy hat, sunglasses, a warm coat, jeans, and leather gloves not because he is genetically predisposed to do so, but because of the point in time, geography, and society in which he lives.

wear — sandals or stilettos, skirt or sari, ball cap or beret — depends upon the point in time, geography, and society in which they live, not their genes. The same can be said for human variation in music making, games, eating patterns, and every other category of behavior both mundane and special.

Another relevant concern, touched upon earlier in this chapter but important enough to review here, is that what we perceive to be human traits are social constructions, not empirical facts. European colonialists of the 16th century viewed skin color as a defining human trait (humans had light skin). During the Inquisition the Spanish viewed religion as a human trait (humans were Catholic). In the early twentieth century, scientists considered attraction to sea faring (so-called *thalassophilia*) a human trait. The point is that some traits that domi-

nate behavioral genetics research today — "impulsivity" for example — may turn out to be misdirections.

Notes

1 See Brophy, K., *et al.* (2002).

2 See Smalley, S. L., *et al.* (2002).

3 Karen LeBacqz, Professor of Theological Ethics, Pacific School of Religion, statement at meeting of the Hastings Center Behavioral Genetics Working Group, May 2002.

4 See Benjamin, J. *et al.* (1996) and Ebstein, R. P. *et al.* (1996).

5 See Kluger, A. N. *et al.* (2002).

6 Task Force on DSM-IV and the American Psychiatric Association. *Diagnostic and Statistical Manual DSM-IV-TR (Text Revision)*. 4th edition, American Psychiatric Association (2002).

7 Caspi, A. *et al.* (2000).

8 See abstract for Rhee, S. H. and I. D. Waldman (2002).

9 Jacobs, P.A., et al. (1965). The XYY story and its ramifications (discussed in the next section) are described in Beckwith, J. (2002) and Nuffield Council on Bioethics (2002).

10 Brunner, H. G. *et al.* (1993).

11 Caspi, A. *et al.* (2002).

12 Quoted in Wasserman, D. (2001, pg. 306); see also Gottesman, I. I. and H. H. Goldsmith (1994).

RESOURCES FOR CHAPTER 6

"ADHD gene discovered: Attention deficit more common in kids with 'snap-25' mutation." 2002. (Accessed 16 December); available at at Webmed.lycos.com/content/article/50/40533.htm.

Barkley, R. 1998. "Attention-deficit hyperactivity disorder." *Scientific American.* (Accessed 10 May, 2001); available at http://www.sciam.com/1998/0998issue/0998barkley.htm.

Beckwith. J. 2002. *Making genes, making waves.* Cambridge, MA: Harvard University Press.

Benjamin J., L. Li, C. Patterson, B. D. Greenberg, D. L. Murphy, and D. H. Hamer. 1996. "Population and familial association between the D4 receptor gene and measures of novelty seeking." *Nature Genetics* 12: 81-84.

Brophy, K., Z. Hawi, A. Kirley, M. Fitzgerald, and M. Gill. 2002. "Synaptosomal-associated protein 25 (SNAP-25) and attention deficit hyperactivity disorder (ADHD): evidence of linkage and association in the Irish population." *Molecular Psychiatry* 7: 913-917.

Brunner, H. G., M. Nelen, X. O. Breakefield, H. H Ropers, and B. A. van Oost. 1993. "Abnormal behavior associated with a point mutation in the structural gene for monoamine oxidase A." *Science* 262: 578-583.

Caspi, A., J. McClay, T. E. Moffitt, J. Mill, J. Martin, I. W. Craig, A. Taylor, and R. Poulton. 2002. "Role of genotype in the cycle of violence in maltreated children." *Science* 297: 851-854.

Caspi, A., A. Taylor, T.E. Moffitt, and R. Plomin. (2000). "Neighborhood deprivation affects children's mental health: Environmental risks identified in a genetic design." *Psychological Science* 11: 338-342.

DeNoon, D. "ADHD gene discovered." 2002. (Accessed 16 December); available at http://www.Webmd.lycos.com/content/article/50/40533.htm.

Duster, T. Forthcoming. "Social context and behavior genetics: Search warrants for research into race, impulsivity, and violence," in Parens, E., A. Chapman, and N. Press (eds.), *Wrestling with Behavioral Genetics: Implications for Understanding Selves and Society.*

Ebstein, R. P., O. Novick, R. Umansky, B. Priel, Y. Osher, D. Blaine, E. R. Bennett, et al. 1996. "Dopamine D4 (D4DR) exon III polymorphism associated with the human personality trait of novelty seeking." *Nature Genetics* 12: 78-80.

Edgar, H. Forthcoming. "Impulsivity, responsibility, and the criminal law," in Parens, E., A. Chapman, and N. Press (eds.), *Wrestling with Behavioral Genetics: Implications for Understanding Selves and Society.*

Federal Bureau of Investigation. 2002. "CODIS mission statement & background." (Accessed 20 December); available at http://www.fbi.gov/hq/lab/codis/program.htm.

Friends Committee on National Legislation website. 2003. "Talking points I: Domestic security enhancement act of 2003 ('Patriot II')." (Accessed 24 May); available at http://www.fcnl.org/issues/immigrant/sup/patriot-2_tlkpts.htm.

Gold, M. 2003. "Va. to begin taking DNA after arrests for felonies." *Washington Post* 1 January, B-1.

Gottesman, I. I. 2002. "Genes and impulsivity – an overview." (Unpublished, personal communication to the Hastings Center Behavior Genetics Working Group).

Gottesman, I. I., and H. H. Goldsmith. 1994. "Developmental psychopathology of antisocial behavior: Inserting genes into its ontogenesis and epigenesis." *Threats to optimal development: Integrating biological, psychological, and social risk factors* Hillsdale, N.J.: Erlbaum.

Harris, D. A. 1999. "Driving while black: Racial profiling on our nation's highways." American Civil Liberties Union Special Report. (Accessed 1 July); available at http://archive.aclu.org/profiling/report.

Jacobs, P.A., M. Brunton, M. M. Melville, R. P. Brittain, and W. F. McClermont. 1965. "Aggressive behaviour, mental subnormality and the XYY male." *Nature* 208: 1351-2.

Kluger A. N., Z. Siegfried, and R. P. Ebstein. 2002. "A meta-analysis of the association between DRD4 polymorphism and novelty seeking." *Molecular Psychiatry.* 7: 712-717.

Mayes, R. 2002. "Rise of ADHD prevalence and psychostimulant use: A historical perspective." American Public Health Association conference, abstract for the 131st Annual Meeting, November 15-19, 2003. (Accessed 19 December 2002); available at http://apha.confex.com/apha/130am/techprogram/paper_46109.htm.

McGough, J., T. McCracken , I. L. MacPhie, C. Francks, S. E. Fisher, R. M. Cantor, A. P. Monaco, and S. F. Nelson. 2002. "Genetic linkage of Attention-Deficit/Hyperactivity Disorder (ADHD) on chromosome 16p13 in a region implicated in autism." *American Journal of Human Genetics* 71: 959-963.

Morrison. J. 2002. "Complete DSM-IV criteria for mental disorders." (Accessed 18 December); available at http://www.geocities.com/morrison94/.

Nuffield Council on Bioethics. 2002. Chapter 9: "Antisocial behavior" in *Genetics and Human Behaviour*. London: Nuffield Council on Bioethics.

Office of Juvenile Justice and Delinquency Prevention. 1999. "Literature review 1999, Part 1: Strengthening America's families: Exemplary parenting and family strategies for delinquency prevention." (Accessed 18 February, 2003); available at http://www.strengtheningfamilies.org/html/lit_review_1999_toc.html

Payawal, E. 1999. "Monoamine oxidase and its affects [sic] on the brain." (Accessed 19 December 2002); available at http://www.ecit.emory.edu/ECIT/chem_ram/MAO/MAO%20WEB.htm#Criminality.

Plomin, R., J. C. DeFries, G. E. McClearn, and M. Rutter. 1997. *Behavioral genetics*, 3rd ed. New York: Freeman Press.

Press, N. Forthcoming. "Social construction and medicalization: Behavioral genetics in context," in Parens, E., A. Chapman, and N. Press (eds.), *Wrestling with Behavioral Genetics: Implications for Understanding Selves and Society*.

Rhee, S, H. and I. D. Waldman. 2002. "Genetic and environmental influences on antisocial behavior: A meta-analysis of twin and adoption studies." *Psychological Bulletin* 128: 490-529.

Sabbatini, R. M. E. 1997. "The history of lobotomy," excerpted from "The History of Psychosurgery." *Brain & Mind Magazine*, June. (Accessed 21 December 2002); available at http://www.epub.org.br/cm/n02/historia/lobotomy.htm.

Schaffner, K. Forthcoming. "Behaving: Its nature and nurture," in Parens, E., A. Chapman, and N. Press (eds.), *Wrestling with Behavioral Genetics: Implications for Understanding Selves and Society*.

Smalley, S. L., V. Kustanovich, S. L. Minassian, J. L. Stone, M. N. Ogdie, J. J. McGough, J. T. McCracken, I. L. MacPhie, C. Francks, S. E. Fisher, R. M. Cantor, A. P. Monaco, and S. F. Nelson., 2002. "Genetic Linkage of Attention-Deficit/Hyperactivity Disorder on Chromosome 16p13, in a Region Implicated in Autism." *American Journal of Human Geneticss* 71: 959-963.

Wasserman, D. 2001. "Responsibility, character, and identity" in *Genetics and Criminal Behavior*. Cambridge, MA: Cambridge University Press.

Wilson, W. H., and K. A. Trott. 2002. "Psychiatric illness associated with criminality." (Accessed 18 December); available at http://www.emedicine.com/med/topic3485.htm.

chapter seven

HOW IS INTELLECT MOLDED BY GENES AND ENVIRONMENTS?

■ ■ ■ Mr. Huang, a puzzled patriarch

Last night, Mr. and Mrs. Huang were introduced to their future daughter-in-law, Vivian Lee. They had been eager to meet the woman whom their son Frank had met in medical school. Frank had told them that Vivian graduated first in her class at a private high school and held a biology degree from Harvard. He also had said that Vivian was from a well-to-do family: her father is a banker and her mother a university professor.

The Huangs liked what they heard about Vivian because they both come from high-achieving families. However, when they met her they had a bit of a shock. The Huangs, who are of Chinese descent, had assumed that Vivian was Chinese, too. This had been a realistic assumption because Frank had always dated Chinese girls before and he knew that his parents wanted him to marry within their culture. Besides, Vivian's surname is Lee.

Last night, one look at the girl told them she was different from what they had expected. It turns out her father is a descendent of Irish immigrants. Her mother is a descendent of Kikiyu Kenyans. The Huangs quickly overcame their surprise and greeted Vivian warmly. They enjoyed their evening with Frank and his fiancée, and of course have no intention of undermining the couple's engagement.

But reading the newspaper at breakfast this morning, Mr. Huang wonders about the direction in which his family tree is bending. The paper contains an article about research into intelligence. Among other things, the article reported that both White Americans and Black Americans fare less well on IQ tests, on average, than Asian Americans.

For a brief moment Mr. Huang wonders if his future grandchildren will be less intelligent than any children Frank would have with a Chinese woman. He immediately dismisses this notion as ridiculous speculation and feels bad for even thinking it.

Focusing back on the facts, Mr. Huang reminds himself that average IQ scores by race do not tell much about how individuals achieve, particularly individuals like his grandchildren who aren't even born yet. What might be more indicative, Mr. Huang ponders, is the fact that Vivian herself is highly intelligent. She has had a good upbringing and the best possible education. She and Frank are in an excellent position to raise their own children into intelligent, successful adults. Those children will have a mix of European, African, and Asian ancestry, but so what? What possible effect could that have on inborn brainpower?

Defining intelligence

Smart. Quick-witted. Sharp. Clever. Astute. The English language has many words that describe intelligence, which briefly defined is the ability to absorb, process, recollect, and apply information. Cognition is the word used by scientists to specifically refer to the process of thinking.

Certainly one reason why there are so many ways to describe intelligence is that the trait involves so many applications of the mind. Intelligence has to do with the ability to reason, to think abstractly, to draw conclusions, to solve problems, to learn from experience, and to remember what has been learned. It also has to do with how the mind makes use of sensory information and how it takes cues from emotions (our own and others'). Thus intelligence is a general capacity of the brain.

Intelligence stands on its own as a trait, but it also permeates all other aspects of personality. Sense of humor, risk-taking tendencies, and sexual attractiveness are just three examples of the many human traits that relate to intelligence.

Intelligence very clearly correlates with successes in school and work settings. Somewhat surprisingly, intelligence also correlates with overall success in living. Less delinquency, greater wealth, better coping skills, higher income, better health, fewer accidental deaths, and longevity are all associated with higher intelligence, according to research. "Bright people have a tail wind in virtually all aspects of life," claims one researcher.[1]

History of intelligence testing

Intelligence has been more intensely studied than any other behavioral trait. Intelligence tests, first developed in the 19th century, have been so heavily researched, refined, and applied that the ones used today are fair predictors (though by no means complete predictors) of academic and professional achievement. Many scientists believe them to be "among the most accurate (in technical terms, reliable and valid) of all psychological tests and assessments."[2]

Some researchers believe that "intelligence" acts like a wind in the sails, pushing one toward success in all aspects of life. Whether intelligence actually has that effect, and why, requires further research.

Francis Galton is the father of the genetically based research into intelligence. His 1869 book *Hereditary Genius* is hailed as "the first quantitative analysis of human mental ability."[3] Galton proposed that human mental ability is an inherited trait and that individual "genius" (as he called it) varies along a continuum from very dull to very bright; the percentage of the population at any point on the continuum decreases as the extremes are approached. Galton was describing a normal curve of distribution, popularly known as the bell curve. His idea about a range for human intelligence was novel at a time when it was generally believed most people had the same intelligence, with just a few being exceptionally slow- or quick-witted.

To explore the connection between intelligence and inheritance, Galton selected for study men of high stature in their respective profession – the law, literature, science, the military, and so forth. He assumed that high achievement in a field correlated with high mental ability. He then observed how frequently the first, second, and third-degree relatives of his selected subjects also achieved high standing in their fields. He compared these frequencies to that which could be expected based on a normal curve of distribution for intelligence. Galton discovered that high achievers did in fact cluster in certain families, and concluded that genius was therefore hereditary.

An early researcher into intelligence, Francis Galton, proposed that eminence in a profession was an indication of mental ability; when he was able to show that certain families had more than a normal number of eminent members, he concluded that mental abilities run in families. At the time (1869), this was a radical idea.

Inspired by Galton's theories, other scientists began to devise tests for intelligence. One of these was the French psychologist, Alfred Binet. By trial-and-error experiments with schoolchildren, both normal and mentally handicapped, Binet deduced what the average child could accomplish at each age level. Binet teamed up with another psychologist, Theodore Simon, to create a test used by French school administrators to identify children less able to profit from instruction in regular school classrooms.

The Binet-Simon scale included 30 tasks such as shaking hands, finding rhymes for words, repeating back a sequence of random digits, and answering logic questions. Performance on the tests was evaluated to determine mental age. According to the Binet-Simon scale, a child had the mental age of 12 if he or she could accomplish the tasks that matched the abilities of the average 12-year-old.

In the early 20th century, a German psychologist named Wilhelm Stern came up with the idea of stating intelligence in terms of the ratio of mental to chronological age. The popular label for this ratio, intelligence quotient or IQ, was coined later by Lewis Terman, an American psychologist. Terman was a member of a committee assigned with the task of developing intelligence tests that could be used to help sort the large number of World War I inductees into appropriate assignments.

Intelligence tests gained in popularity after that war. The military continued to use them for recruitment and placement purposes, and workplaces and schools started to use them, too. Social scientists conducted IQ tests to support theories about which types of people were more or less intelligent. At this point in American history, slavery had been abolished less than a hundred years earlier and waves of new immigrants were coming into the country. Much was made over the weak IQ performance of American Blacks and of immigrants from Eastern Europe.

In the latter part of the 20th century, controversy arose over whether intelligence tests were biased. Some questioned Galton's original work by pointing out that high professional achievement may have less to do with inborn intelligence than with having the means for education and social connections. Other critics noted that performance on IQ tests most accurately reflects whether you can read the language of the test and are familiar

In the early twentieth century, laws restricted immigration from Eastern Europe, based in part on the false belief that such people would dilute the intelligence of the American population.

ARRIVING AT ELLIS ISLAND

Today, performance on IQ tests is considered a reasonable predictor of success. IQ scores correlate reasonably well, though imperfectly, with academic and professional achievement and they correlate to a lesser extent, though more than randomly, with success in social and personal aspects of life.

Employers, the armed forces, colleges, and other important social institutions make use of intelligence and aptitude tests to screen and place applicants.

Measuring *g*

Many intelligence researchers accept the theory that there is some underlying ability to learn that feeds into all cognitive performance. This ability is called *g*. The term stands for general cognitive ability. The concept of *g* was first articulated more than 100 years ago by Charles Spearman, a British psychologist, and it refers to a basic, core ability to make use of information. Some researchers refer to *g* by two other eponymous terms, "global factor" and "general intelligence factor." Scientists debate whether *g* is an actual property of the brain such as some neurological mechanism at work (the minority view) or merely an abstract property like "horsepower" (the majority view).

The concept of *g* derives from the observation that any given individual tends to perform at about the same level on a diverse range of intelligence tests. Whether you give someone a math test or a vocabulary test, an oral test or a pen-and-paper test, a test with words or a test with pictures, a timed test or an untimed test: across all types of tests, most people

with facts from the culture of those who create these tests. Critics also claimed that scientists were interpreting data in ways that supported their pre-existing racial and cultural prejudices.

Advocates took some of these concerns to heart and sought to create less biased, more accurate tests. Many tests have been developed, each using a different selection of tasks to measure intelligence in its various manifestations: mastery of vocabulary; text comprehension; math skills; memory; visual acumen; understanding of universal concepts such as up/down and in/out; grasp of general knowledge; speed of response; application of logic; and more. These tests continue to have an enormous role in modern society. This is particularly true in education, as attested to by the widespread use of the SAT and other tests that measure scholastic aptitude.

score somewhat consistently.

A statistical procedure called factor analysis is applied to scores on a variety of tests, weighting each differently according to the complexity of the test's cognitive demands, to arrive at a number for this pattern of consistency. That number is called g, and it is roughly equivalent to IQ, but is considered slightly more pure. This is because the pooling of data from many types of tests dilutes the possibility that what is being measured is a specific set of learned skills rather than a basic aptitude.

Across IQ tests, *g* accounts for about 40 percent of the variance in performance. Within any single test, most of the variance is independent of *g*. The significance of that anomaly is that *g* is not the only factor involved in cognition.

Some researchers have added a refine-ment to the theory of *g*. They suggest that *g* is comprised of distinct subsets of cognitive ability including fluid intelligence (abstract reasoning), crystallized intelligence (vocabulary and general knowledge), visual-spatial ability, memory, and speed of processing. This theory is also based on factor analysis: an individual's scores on *certain types* of intelligence tests tend to correlate more highly compared to the correlation of that individual's scores on *all types* of tests.

An alternative to the notion of *g* is the idea that intelligence spans many different human abilities. One such theory of multiple intelligences (proposed by Howard Gardner in 1983) holds that humans have eight forms of intelligence: linguistic, logical-mathematical, spatial, kinesthetic, musical, intrapersonal, inter-personal, and naturalist. Other similar

Researchers have observed that some people apply mathematical calculations and other problem-solving skills in real-life situations much better than they do on IQ tests.

theories propose different cognitive domains. The multiple intelligences theory raises the possibility that measurements of *g* capture some, but not all, aspects of intelligence, and that it may not be possible to comprehensively measure the trait in full.

Other researchers are highly critical of the whole concept. Some argue that the construct of *g* is of no value in the search for the underlying neurobiological processes that contribute to cognition. One scientist has decried "the unreality of *g* and the fallacy of regarding intelligence as a single-scaled, innate thing in the head."[4] Critics point out that if you alter the underlying assumptions used in factor analysis, no single number *g* emerges. They believe that the positive correlations in an individual's performance on various IQ tests do not have to do with any underlying factor, but rather simply reflect the individual's life circumstances. They assert that someone who is well fed, adequately sheltered, educated, and expected by family and peers to achieve, will do well on most tasks set before him or her. Someone in opposite circumstances will not do as well, across the board.

Some suggest that *g* only reflects test-taking skills, not intelligence as it is used in real life. For example, the social anthropologist Jean Lave has observed that poor favela children in Rio de Janeiro easily do arithmetic when selling wares on the street but perform miserably when asked

to add and subtract in a classroom. By the same token, Liberian tailors are able to make precise arithmetic calculations when measuring customers but cannot do the same when tested.

This idea of multiple intelligences was first raised in the 1950s, about half a century after *g* was proposed. It has not been as extensively applied and researched as *g*. Indeed, among many scientists researching intelligence today, *g* is considered beyond dispute. *g* is the core piece of data used in analyses that compare the intelligence of individuals and groups. If the critics are correct, however — if there is no *g* — then many of the conclusions drawn from intelligence research will have to be revisited. The reader is advised to keep this in mind while reading the next sections of this chapter.

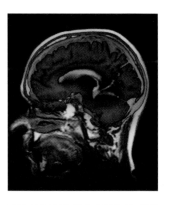

g is the ability to learn that underlies all cognitive performance. Some researchers are seeking the genetic contributors to *g*, while others question whether *g* is actually a real or useful concept.

Quantitative research into intelligence

A great many quantitative studies have shown that IQ correlation increases as genetic similarity increases. Quantitative studies also provide evidence of environmental influences on intelligence:

- In studies of identical twins raised together, IQ scores do not correlate completely. You would expect near-perfect correlation between genetic equals if IQ were solely hereditary.
- In studies comparing blood relatives raised together to those raised separately, the IQ scores of the former tend

to be more similar than those of the latter.

- In studies of family members not related by blood (for example, parents and their adopted children), there is modest, but statistically significant, correlations of IQ scores.

Most quantitative studies of intelligence measuring modern Western populations have produced heritability estimates ranging broadly around 0.50. Taken together, they suggest that genetics and environment are roughly equivalent in their influence on the variation in IQ.

The relative contributions of the shared and the non-shared environment also have been partitioned out in heritability estimates, and this had led to one surprising bit of data. Compared to most other behavioral traits, intelligence in childhood seems to be more significantly shaped by the shared environment compared to the nonshared environment. This could possibly mean that the home environment has a greater influence on a child's cognitive development than on other characteristics, such as personality.

Researchers are interested in how the contributions of genes and environment change over time. Do inherited characteristics become more important as one gets older, or does the influence of the environment become more important? Most studies of IQ kinship correlations show that genetic influence grows and shared environmental influence falls away almost completely.

One possibility is that heritability increases with age because of genotype-environment correlation. That is, as people grow up they are able to exert more control over their experiences. For example, children with higher innate intelligence might choose to engage in activities that stimulate their intellect such as pursuing formal education, reading, spending time in stimulating conversation, and engaging in work that challenges the mind. By contrast, children with lower innate intelligence might gravitate towards non-intellectual activities. Thus, genetic tendencies would be reinforced over time.

The opposite possibility is that the effects of the environment become stronger as one gets older. Under this scenario, children who grow up in stimulating homes and who attend quality preschools would follow a higher intellectual trajectory than children whose early years are less supportive. They would get better grades in school, have a better chance of making it to college and have more motivation to enroll there, have the academic credentials to obtain intellectually-challenging jobs, etc. Thus, the effects of early environment would become magnified over time.

Another possibility is that the relative contributions of genes and environment remain stable over the lifetime. In 1997, data supporting this hypothesis emerged from a study of 240 pairs of Swedish twins in their eighties. In this study, the heritability of general cognitive ability was computed at 0.62.[5] This is relatively close to the heritability estimates from studies of younger subjects and thus supports the proposition that the heritability of IQ does not shift significantly with age. More research is needed before the question of how intelligence is affected by genes relative to environment over time can be answered.

Well-nurtured and stimulated children tend to perform better on IQ tests than children who lack such benefits. This is evidence for the environmental contribution to intelligence.

Molecular research into intelligence

As the careful reader should realize by now, twin studies tell us nothing specific about the genetic and environmental factors underlying intelligence. Molecular research seeks to bridge this gap, at least in terms of identifying genetic contributors to intelligence; in turn this may aid in the search for environmental contributors.

The operating assumption is that cognition is a complex trait with many genes involved, each of relatively small effect. There are exceptions to this general rule. As we described in earlier chapters, some people acquire damage to their brains, significantly affecting their intelligence, from disorders such as PKU, Fragile X, and early-onset Alzheimer's. Each of these

Endophenotypes are the underlying processes to a trait. For example, for the trait of intelligence, endophenotypes might include speed of information processing, capacity of working memory, and other traits. A useful analogy can be found in the component parts of home construction such as bricks, lumber, and tools.

disorders stem from problem alleles in a single gene.

The general rule, however, is that cognitive abilities are shaped by a multitude of genetic and environmental factors that interweave throughout development. It is estimated that any single gene accounts for at best 1 to 2 percent of the variation in intelligence; discrete environmental factors likely make similarly modest contributions. This means that highly intelligent people are blessed not with one brainy gene, but rather with an abundance of "positive alleles for high g," as some researchers refer to them.[6] They may also have experienced favorable nutritional and nurturing conditions during their development and/or been raised in an environment conducive to intellectual growth. Persons with lower intellect may possess an inordinate amount of "negative alleles for high g," may have experienced unfavorable conditions during their development, and/or may have been raised in intellectually unsupportive environments.

Genes and environment interacting through processes of development form a triple whammy: anyone who comes up favorably in all three categories has a strong likelihood of high g. Anyone who comes up short across the board has a strong likelihood of low g. For those with a middling assortment, the likely range for g is much broader.

To focus back on just the genetic contributors to intelligence: one way to imagine the variety of genes involved in a trait like intelligence is to picture the different products involved in the structure of a house. Concrete, plaster, wood, plastic, nails, glass, metal — each serves a different purpose, yet contributes to the overall structure. Endophenotypes are the equivalents of the products that make a house. They are the intermediate traits, the underlying processes that contribute to a phenotype. For cognition, these endophenotypes would include such things as speed of information processing, capacity of working memory, synapse dexterity, receptor functionality, and a great many more elements of brain activity. (A diagram illustrating endophenotypes appears on page 86.)

To use another metaphor, just as tiny rivulets running down a mountain join together into a mighty stream, each relevant gene contributes to the causal pathway by which intelligence is formed. For genetic researchers, the concept of endophenotypes narrows and makes more manageable the search for relevant genes. Using genomic scans or association studies, they can look for correlations between tiny but discrete aspects of brain function and specific alleles of single genes. This is how several candidates for "IQ genes" have been identified.

The quest to find the individual genes that contribute in some small but measurable way to intelligence bring to mind an old Chinese proverb: "In vain do men seek the source of great rivers." Despite formidable obstacles, some researchers are pursuing this quest. Hundreds of molecular studies have been conducted, and several genes contributing to cognitive function have been tentatively identified in humans, mice, and even in fruit flies.

One such gene achieved some prominence in a 1998 study. Named IGF2R, the gene is on Chromosome 6 and is an acronym for "insulin-like growth factor-2 receptor." Insulin-like growth factors are hormones that affect the work of the nervous system. In this particular study, researchers conducted scans of a segment of Chromosome 6 in high-IQ children and a control group of children. A tiny but significant proportion of the high-IQ children were found to have a particular allele for IGF2R, Allele 5, compared to the control group children. Allele 5 also was found in slightly greater proportion in tests on children with extremely high IQs, high mathematical ability, and high verbal ability.[7]

A follow-up study by the same researchers failed to confirm the hypothesis that the IGF2R gene is associated with cognition.[8] Other genes proposed as candidate "IQ genes" have not been confirmed, either. But the point of this research is not only to discover the particular genes that help shape intelligence. It also is to understand how intelligence is affected by an overall biological/environmental/developmental process in which genes play a part. For example, there is speculation that insulin may play a role in

learning and memory. Investigations into IGF2R, whether or not they confirm this particular gene as having anything to do with intelligence, may shed light on how insulin figures in cognition. Following the trail of other implicated genes may offer new insights into how intelligence emerges in human beings.

Predicting individual intelligence

Molecular research sheds light on genetic inputs, but not on specific individuals. IGF2R gene researchers made this very point in their published results. They specifically noted that more than half of the high-IQ children *did not* have Allele 5 for IGF2R, while almost a quarter of the control-group children *did*. When and if the gene IGF2R is confirmed as having a role in IQ, it will not be a signpost for who's bright and who's not. It may, however, be recognized as an intelligence susceptibility gene.

Suppose molecular researchers someday identify the scores of genes that weave together into cognition. They further identify the "positive" and "negative" alleles for each gene. Then they do a genome scan of an individual to count the number of "positive alleles" present. They still will not be able to state with certitude anything about that person's intellectual abilities. Scientists might be able to offer a likely range for that individual's intelligence, but it would be a

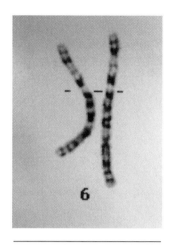

Several genes have been investigated as being potentially involved in intelligence, including one called IGF2R, located on Chromosome 6. None of the candidate genes has been confirmed. In any event, there is certain to be a great number of genes involved.

Even if you are born with weak eyesight, your vision can get close to perfect using corrective procedures and lenses. In the same way, even if you are born with "weak" intelligence, environmental interventions can boost your brainpower dramatically.

supportive environments may be able to build intellect even in individuals bequeathed with a relatively poor set of genetic material. Some researchers speculate that the environment during prenatal and early childhood development are particularly important factors for intelligence. A child who receives adequate nutrition in the womb, is nurtured and stimulated as a baby, and is exposed to early education can obtain important boosts to cognition.

One psychologist asserts, "We have demonstrated that intellectual skills often believed to be innate are extremely sensitive to the environment." [9] This psychologist has conducted research that produced correlations between the verbal stimulation provided by parents and the vocabulary and grammatical dexterity acquired by children. Other researchers have found correlations between many other specific environmental conditions and intelligence.[10] But the key word here is correlation. Researchers have not yet found a way to move beyond correlation to identify discrete environmental equivalents of genes that mold behavior.

Even if every genetic and environmental input were identified, prediction will never be perfectible. To understand why, think about weather forecasting. Meteorologists today make use of a great deal of data concerning atmosphere, terrain, precipitation, temperature, ocean currents, and all the other discrete variables that coalesce into rain on this side

guess all the same. This is because genes are probabilistic, not deterministic, for the reason that should be obvious by now to the reader — they operate within environments over time.

Eyesight makes a useful example here. Presume that nearsightedness is a genetic trait. If you inherit your father's nearsightedness, a pair of eyeglasses can correct your vision to 20:20. In the same way, of the mountain and sunshine on the other. As a result, weather prediction is more accurate than it used to be, but because of the nonsystematic way these variables interact it may never be exact. Similarly, as scientists learn more about the processes by which genes and environment interact over time, they might get better at predicting individual intelligence. Yet, because the inputs are nonsystematic, such predictions will never be precise and sometimes they will be really wrong.

Mr. Huang's speculations

Many studies have analyzed academic achievement by race. This research may be of interest to Mr. Huang, who is wondering about the cognitive prospects of future children born to his son, who is of Asian descent, and his future daughter-in-law, who has European and African ancestry.

There is reason to believe that race and intelligence are not related biologically. Important data on this point comes from The National Collaborative Perinatal Project, a study that began in 1959. Some 48,000 pregnant women were enrolled from several major U.S. cities. A roughly equal number of Black and White participants were involved. Importantly, the socioeconomic status (SES) of the subjects covered a broad span. SES refers to one's position within a hierarchical social structure, and it is determined by several variables including occupation, education, income, wealth, and place of residence. The original intention of this study was to learn about cerebral palsy and other health complications from childbirth, not intelligence. However, many thousands of pieces of data were collected on the subjects, including IQ scores for the more than 59,000 children born to these mothers, obtained at ages four and seven. According to this data, when sorted by SES there is very little difference in IQ between Black and White children.[11]

Despite the significance of this finding, it has rarely been cited in scholarly papers on intelligence. What has gained more prominence is other IQ testing data collected before and since (mostly from subjects in the upper tiers of SES) and pooled together to draw bell curves for the population as a whole as well as for various subgroups.

Black children given IQ tests score similarly to White children of the same socioeconomic status.

Looking at these bell curves, Mr. Huang might be relieved to learn that people of all races and ethnicities can be found at every IQ level, including the high end of the curve. On the other hand, Mr. Huang might be disturbed to learn that the bell curve for White Americans is centered somewhat lower compared to East Asians and Jews. The bell curve for Black Americans and Hispanics sits even lower. Mr. Huang also might be troubled by U.S. Census Bureau data indicating that, compared to Asian Americans, a smaller percentage of White and Black Americans complete high school, have college degrees, and are in professional or managerial jobs.

Whites do better than Asians on some measures; for example, their unemployment rate is lower and their home ownership rate is higher. But Blacks do worse than both Asians and Whites on several measures. For example, even when Blacks and Whites achieve equally well on standardized tests such as the SAT, the former are outperformed by the latter academically. Grade point average is lower, they drop out of school at higher rates, and the time to graduation is longer. This has been called the over-prediction phenomenon: for Blacks, performance on standardized tests over-predicts their academic achievement compared to Whites with the same score. In other words, even when Blacks are as well *prepared* academically as Whites, they do not *perform* as well academically.

Education is highly revered in Chinese and Japanese cultures. This could explain in part why Chinese-American and Japanese-American children, as groups, tend to do well in school.

Accounting for disparities in population IQs

The discrepancies described above have been used by some people to argue that there is an intrinsic, biological difference between people of different racial and ethnic groups. "Most experts believe that environment is important in pushing the bell curves apart, but that genetics could be involved too," according to an essay on intelligence signed by a large number of researchers in the field and published in the *Wall Street Journal* in 1994.[12]

There are many possible explanations for how the environment pushes the bell curves apart. It is speculated that the Asian culture's emphasis on achievement could account, in part, for the comparatively higher I.Q. performance of Asian Americans. It should be noted here that "Asian American" is a very broad term that encompasses Asian Indian, Bangladeshi, Cambodian, Chinese, Filipino, Hmong, Indonesian, Japanese, Korean, Laotian, Pakistani, Thai, Taiwanese, Vietnamese, and others.

Of these groups, the "model minority" label best fits Chinese and Japanese Americans because they rank so highly on various measures of achievement. Different immigration experiences could explain the much lower levels of achievement for other Asian American populations. Similarly, the immigration struggles of Hispanic Americans might account for their lagging IQ scores relative to Whites and Asians.

The poverty, segregation, and discrimination that African Americans have historically experienced since slavery days and continue to experience could account for their relatively lower achievement, as a group, on IQ. Another recent theory is that African Americans perform less well academically because they succumb to stereotypes about themselves. A number of studies have demonstrated that people's performances suffer when they know they are being watched, when they know that their performance has a consequence (for example, that they might lose a prize), or when they are aware that they are different from others in the test group (for example, if they are the only female being tested in a group of males). Therefore, it could be that the mere fact of being African American in a culture that stereotypes Blacks as inferior may be sufficiently disturbing to impair performance.

Indeed, this is the finding of a groundbreaking study published in 1995. In this experiment, groups of college students

were given a section of the verbal part of the GRE test. Some of the students were told that the test was to measure their ability, while others were told that the test was simply a problem-solving task. Interestingly, Black students underperformed White students only in the groups that had been told their ability was being measured. The researchers ascribed this phenomenon to "stereotype threat." In their words,

> ...whenever African American students perform an explicitly scholastic or intellectual task, they face the threat of confirming or being judged by a negative societal stereotype — a suspicion — about their group's intellectual ability and

Research suggests that academic performance suffers when people feel they are being watched or judged or when they feel something important rides on the results.

competence. This threat is not borne by people not stereotyped in this way. And the self-threat it causes — through a variety of mechanisms — may interfere with the intellectual functioning of these students, particularly during standardized tests.[13]

The researchers also argue that long-term effects on Blacks of stereotype threat may be for them to reject the ideal of academic achievement, to lose interest in achievement, to put less effort into it, and as a result, to achieve less.

Class (which closely parallels race in this country) could be another environmental factor that pushes the bell curves apart. A 2003 study made fresh use of twin data from the National Collaborative Perinatal Project (which, as we mentioned previously, had been underappreciated). The NCPP included so many mothers and their children that it contained data on more than 600 twin pairs. NCCP researchers were able to locate about half of those pairs for IQ testing at

age seven. The new study used the NCCP twin and SES data along with advanced model fitting techniques to parse out the relative contributions of genetics and environment. The researchers concluded that genetic influence varies depending on socioeconomic status.

According to the abstract (summary) of the study, "In impoverished families, 60 percent of the variance in IQ is accounted for by the shared environment, and the contribution of genes is close to zero; in affluent families, the result is almost exactly the reverse." The implication is that the quality of the environment has a swamping effect; impoverished conditions tend to suppress genetic potential, while enriched conditions tend to allow genetic potential to flourish. The study concluded, "Although there is much that remains to be understood, our study and the ones that have preceded it have begun to converge on the hypothesis that the developmental forces at work in poor environments are qualitatively different from those at work in adequate ones."[14]

How would genetics push the bell curves apart? It would mean that "positive alleles for g" are more preponderant in one racial group than another. Such differences among geographically dispersed human populations could conceivably have occurred through the forces of natural selection.

Since environments and genetics work together over development, the human group that achieves best on intellectual

Based on twin studies, researchers have suggested that the environment may have a greater impact on the development of intelligence for children raised in impoverished environments compared to those raised in rich environments.

scales would be the one that has advantage in both environmental and genetic departments. And so while one could speculate that Asian Americans have a greater assortment of "positive alleles for g" than any other racial or ethnic group, alternate hypotheses also could be proposed. For example, it could be that Asian Americans are not more gifted genetically than other groups, but they are advantaged environmentally. Or it could be that African Americans are so disadvantaged environmentally that their equivalent or even superior genetic gifts cannot make up the difference.

But this is all speculation. The difficulty in researching racial differences in cognition lies in the fact that racial identifications are less a biological fact than a social construct. Population genetics is the branch of science concerned with gene frequencies — the prevalence of alleles in populations. As any population geneticist will tell you, there is more genetic diversity between individuals of one population than there is between population groups. A White person from Denmark may be more similar genetically to a Black person from Sudan than to another White Dane. Your "race" (as determined by your own choice or as assigned by others) yields less data useful to behavior research than specific information about your particular biological ancestors.

Yet considered on a statistical basis, some alleles do occur more frequently in some racial and ethnic populations.

As a well-known example, the alleles that lead to the blood disorders of sickle cell disease and thalassemia appear more frequently in African and Mediterranean populations, respectively. Such facts justify the quest pursued by some researchers to discover the "IQ genes" that would explain why some racial and ethnic groups dominate in intelligence testing and achievement.

Researchers might be able to obtain usable data on the race and intelligence question through molecular techniques. For example, it may be possible to determine ancestry of subjects through DNA analysis, give them intelligence tests (that are not culturally biased), and see how those whose lineage traces back to Asia perform on these tests compared to those whose ancestors come from Europe or Africa.

In the final analysis, though, the answers will have to do with populations, not individuals. Mr. Huang cares not about how Asian Americans, White Americans, or Black Americans fare as groups in terms of intelligence. He cares about the potential of his individual, mixed-race American grandchildren.

It is possible for two people of different races to be more related genetically to each other than they are to some people from their own respective race.

Perhaps some day, when scores of susceptibility genes for IQ have been identified, microarray analysis could determine the number of alleles associated with high cognitive capabilities that are possessed by Mr. Huang's descendents. That is not yet possible. Even if it were, the data would produce only a measure of probable potential. What happens over time with that potential — whether it is maximized or wasted — remains outside anyone's full control.

Eugenic concerns

In an ideal world, Mr. Huang would never even entertain the notion that a grandchild with a superficial racial difference might have inferior intelligence. But the world in which Mr. Huang lives is not ideal. There is a long history of humans seeking to find distinctions between groups in order to declare that one is better than another.

Francis Galton, cited at the beginning of this chapter as the father of modern genetics, is also the fellow who coined the term eugenics. It comes from the Greek for "well born," and stands for the idea that human races can be improved through selective breeding. Tied to this philosophy is the concern that humanity will degenerate without deliberate intervention. Conceived in noble ideas about the betterment of mankind, in practice twentieth century eugenics was base and shameless.

Eugenics, nurtured in America and other western countries, led to the aggressive promotion of childbearing among educated White women. This is an example of positive eugenics. It also led to the institutionalization of the "unfit" to prevent their procreation and to the extensive use of sterilization on those declared feeble-minded or insane. These are two examples of negative eugenics. Sterilization victims often were poor and/or non-White and in most cases consent was not obtained. In the U.S., more than 40,000 eugenic sterilizations were conducted in thirty states between 1907 and 1944.

Eugenic ideas were adopted to hideous effect by the Nazi government in Germany, which sterilized hundreds of thousands and killed millions on the grounds that they were diseased, of low intelligence, or politically troublesome. They targeted enemies, primarily the Jews, and used eugenic arguments to justify their policies.

After World War II, eugenics fell into disfavor, though some policies such as sterilization remained in effect in a few countries for many more years — in the U.S., through the 1970s. Yet the basic philosophy of eugenics endures. In 1994, controversy over eugenics re-emerged with the publication of *The Bell Curve*. In this book the authors described a "dysgenic trend": the poorly educated were reproducing more rapidly compared to the well educated. The authors claimed that race and class differences in IQ are primarily genetic and immutable.[15] Many people from the fields of genetics, sociology, and statistics have presented strong scientific arguments against these claims. Nonetheless, the debate itself gave fresh sustenance to the perception that race matters.

Genetic discoveries open the door to new ways to practice eugenics. For example, it is now possible to select children based on genetics. Selection techniques fall into two categories: selections for therapeutic reasons — to avoid serious medical disorder — and selections for enhancement — to obtain a desired trait.

DNA can be obtained from fetuses through amniocentesis and other techniques used for prenatal diagnosis, and some parents now use this information to decide whether or not to continue a pregnancy. DNA also can be obtained from embryos created through *in vitro* fertilization, and parents sometimes use this information to select which embryo or embryos to implant in the mother.

At the present time, prenatal diagnosis is used primarily to determine the presence of problem alleles linked to single-gene disorders, so as to avoid giving birth to a child with a fatal illness. For example, in the U.S. standard prenatal care now includes a DNA screening test for cystic fibrosis. Tests for many other diseases will probably become routine in the coming years. It should be mentioned

The Nazis used pseudo-scientific eugenic theories to justify the oppression and mass murder of Jewish people and other non-Aryans. Today, some people fear that behavioral genetic theories could be distorted to advance the idea that some people are better than others.

that prenatal screening today is imperfectly implemented; Cystic fibrosis testing in the United States has resulted in some terminations of healthy fetuses due to misinterpretation of results, according to medical geneticists.[16]

Prenatal diagnosis also can be used to select for sex, either for medical reasons such as if the family has a history of an X-linked medical disorder (in which case they would select for a girl), or if the parents simply prefer to have a child of a particular sex (in which case they most often select for a boy).

It is not possible to genetically select for such behavioral traits as pleasant disposition, athleticism, altruism, or high intelligence. One reason it is not possible is that we do not yet have solid proof about *any* of the genes that play *any* part in these behavioral traits. Even if and when all relevant genes are identified, genetic selection for a behavioral trait will be complicated by the fact that many genes are involved.

Yet as research advances, it may become feasible to identify the many genes associated with a behavioral trait and to engineer embryos to carry all the known "positive alleles" for that trait. Would such engineering actually create a child who grows up to have the desired trait? Possibly yes, but possibly no, because the effects of genes on behavior are determined by their environmental context over the course of development.

A more likely possibility is that enhancement opportunities will be marketed by genetic testing companies before there is any solid scientific basis to their products. This, of course, would be ethically problematic. Many other ethical concerns also attach to the possibility of genetic enhancement for behavioral traits:

- When and if enhancement technology becomes available, who will have access to it – only the rich, or everyone equally?
- Who decides what enhancements are desirable – individuals or society?

- Will parents feel obliged to select for enhancement so as not to disadvantage their child?
- How will selecting for particular traits affect the parent-child relationship?
- What are the psychological, legal, and social ramifications when children do not meet the potential expected by their enhancements?

In the end all such questions may be moot, because complex behavioral traits such as intelligence may be forever beyond our ability to engineer. The more we learn about behavioral genetics, the more likely it seems that we will never be able to completely predict or control how our children think, how well they think, and what they do with their thoughts.

Genetic research could make it possible for parents to pre-select the behavior characteristics of their children – or at least to try. Even if such genetic selection could be done, the unforeseeable effects of the environment would make the results uncertain.

Notes

1 Linda Gottfredson, Professor of Education, University of Delaware, quoted in Holden, C. (2003, pg. 192).

2 Gottfredson, L., *et al.* (1994, pg. 13).

3 Wozniak, R. H. (1999).

4 See Gould, S. J. (1995, pg. 2).

5 See McClearn, G. *et al.* (1997).

6 See, for example, Chorney, M. J. *et al.* (1998).

7 Chorney, M. J. (1998).

8 Hill, L. *et al.* (2002).

9 University of Chicago psychologist Janellen Huttenlocher, quoted in Wickelgren, I. (1999. pg. 1832).

10 See Wickelgren, I. *Ibid.*

11 Nichols, P., and V. Elving Anderson (1973).

12 Gottfredson, L., *et al.* (1997, pg. 15).

13 See Steele, C. M. and J. Aronson (1995, pg. 797).

14 Turkheimer et. al. (2003). Abstract quotation from pg. 623. Study quotation from pg. 628.

15 Herrnstein, R. J., and C. Murray (1994).

16 See Concar, D. (2003).

RESOURCES FOR CHAPTER 7

"Alfred Binet." 2003. (Accessed 26 March); available at http://www.indiana.edu/~intell/binet.html.

Asian-Nation. 2003. "The model minority image." (Accessed 30 June); available at http://www.asian-nation.org/model-minority.shtml.

Chapman, A.R. and M. S. Frankel (eds.), 2003. *Designing Our Descendants: The Promises and Perils of Genetic Modifications.* Baltimore: The Johns Hopkins University Press.

Chorney, M. J., K. Chorney, N. Seese, M. J. Owen, J. Daniels, P. McGuffin, L. A. Thompson, D. K. Detterman, C. Benbow, D. Luninski, T. Eley, and R. Plomin. 1998. "A quantitative trait locus associated with cognitive ability in children." *Psychological Science* 9, no. 3: 159-166.

Concar, D. 3 May 2003. "Test blunders risk needless abortions." *New Scientist* 178: 4.

Gottesmann, I. I. 1997. "Twins: En route to QTLs for cognition." *Science* 276: 1522-1523.

-----. 2003. "The endophenotype concept in psychiatry: etymology and strategic intentions." *American Journal of Psychiatry* 160: 636-645.

Gottfredson, L. 1998. "The general intelligence factor." *Scientific American* (Accessed 31 March 2003); available at http://www.psych.utoronto.ca/.

---. "Mainstream science on intelligence." 1997. Intelligence 24 (1): 13-23. Reprinted from *Wall Street Journal* 13 December 1994 (51 additional signatories).

Gould, S. J. 1995. "Curveball." In *The bell curve wars: Race, intelligence, and the future of America.* Steven Fraser, ed. New York: Basic Books.

Herrnstein, R. J., and C. Murray. 1994. *The bell curve: Intelligence and class structure in American life.* New York: Free Press.

Hill, L., M. J. Chorney, D. Lubinski, L. A. Thompson, and R. Plomin. 2002. "A quantitative trait locus not associated with cognitive ability in children: A failure to replicate." *Psychological Science* 13: 561-562.

Holden, C. 2003. "The practical benefits of general intelligence." *Science* 299: 192-193.

Lave. Jean. 1988. *Cognition in practice: Mind, mathematics, and culture in everyday life.* New York: Cambridge University Press.

Lubinski. 2000. "Intelligence, success and fitness." *Novartis Foundation Symposium 233: The nature of intelligence.* Gregory E. Bock and Jamie A. Goode, eds. Chichester, U.K: John Wiley.

McGue, M., T. J. Bouchard, Jr., W. G. Iacono, and D. T. Lykken. 1993. "Behavioral genetics of cognitive ability: A life-span perspective." In R. Plomin and G.E. McClearn, eds. *Nature, Nurture, and Psychology.* Washington D.C.: American Psychological Association Press, 59-76

McLearn, G. E., B. Johansson, S. Berg, N. L. Pedersen, F. Ahern, S. A. Petrill, R. Plomin. 1997. "Substantial genetic influence on cognitive abilities in twins 80 or more years old." *Science* 276: 1560-1563.

National Center for Education Statistics. 2003. "Dropout rates in the United States: 2000." (Accessed 30 June); available at http://nces.ed.gov/pubs2002/droppub_2001/.

Nichols, P., and V. Elving Anderson. 1973. "Intellectual performance, race, and socioeconomic status." *Social Biology* 20: 367-374.

Nuffield Report. 2003. Chapter 7: "Review of the evidence: Intelligence" and Chapter 13: "Selecting and changing behavioural traits." In *Genetics and human behaviour.* London: Nuffield Council on Bioethics.

Plomin, R. 2003. "Genetics, genes, genomics, and g." *Molecular Psychiatry* 8: 1-5.

Sofair, A. N. and L. C Kaldjian. 2002. "Eugenic sterilization and a qualified Nazi analogy: The United States and Germany, 1930-1945." *Annals of Internal Medicine*: 132: 312-319.

Steele, C. M. and J. Aronson. 1995. "Stereotype threat and the intellectual test performance of African Americans." *Journal of Personality and Social Psychology* 69: 797-811.

Turkheimer, E., A. Haley, M. Waldron, B. D'Onofrio, I. I. Gottesman. 2003. "Socioeconomic status modifies heritability of IQ in young children." *Psychological Science*: 14: 623-628.

Wickelgren, I. 1999. "Nurture helps mold able minds." *Science* 283: 1832-1834.

Wozniak, R. H. 1999. "Francis Galton: Hereditary genius (1869)." Extracted from *Classics in Psychology, 1855–1914: Historical Essays.* Bristol, UK: Thoemmes Press. (Accessed 26 March 2003); available at http://195.12.26.123/psych/galton.htm.

GLOSSARY/INDEX

The numbers after each term represent the chapter in which it first appears.

additive 2
When an allele's contribution to the variation in a phenotype is separately measurable; the independent effects of alleles "add up." Antonym of nonadditive.

ADHD/ADD 6
Attention Deficit Hyperactivity Disorder/Attention Deficit Disorder. Neurobehavioral disorders characterized by an attention span or ability to concentrate that is less than expected for a person's age. With ADHD, there also is age-inappropriate hyperactivity, impulsive behavior or lack of inhibition. There are several types of ADHD: a predominantly inattentive subtype, a predominantly hyperactive-impulsive subtype, and a combined subtype. The condition can be cognitive alone or both cognitive and behavioral.

adoption study 4
A type of research focused on families that include one or more children raised by persons other than their biological parents. In an adoption study, adoptees, their biological parents, their adoptive parents, and/or other members of the biological and adoptive families are assessed for resemblance on a trait. The objective is to determine the relative importance of genetic and environmental influences.

aggression 6
Behavior manifested by destructive and attacking actions, by covert attitudes of hostility and obstructionism, or by a healthy self-expressive drive to mastery. Aggression may arise from innate drives and/or in response to frustration.

allele 2
One of two or more alternative forms of a gene; a single allele for each gene is inherited separately from each parent.

Alzheimer's disease 5
A medical disorder causing the loss of memory, reasoning, and language abilities. Protein residues called plaques and tangles build up and interfere with brain function. This disorder usually first appears in persons over age sixty-five. Compare to early-onset Alzheimer's.

amino acids 2
Molecules that are combined to form proteins. The sequence of amino acids in a protein, and hence protein function, is determined by the genetic code.

amnesia 5
Loss of memory, temporary or permanent, that can result from brain injury, illness, or trauma.

antibodies 2
Proteins produced by immune system cells that bind to microorganisms, such as viruses and bacteria, and inactivate them.

antisocial behavior 6
Acting in a manner that is hostile or harmful to organized society; especially deviating sharply from the social norm.

antisocial personality disorder 6
Medical diagnosis of having a pattern of behaving against the norm or in hostile and harmful ways.

association study 4

Form of molecular research that seeks to test whether the variation in specific DNA sequences might be statistically correlated with the variation in a particular trait. This approach is used to detect genes with relatively small effect on a trait.

autism 5

A complex developmental disability that emerges in early childhood and interferes with the normal development of social skills and communication.

base 2

See nucleotide.

behavior 1

The response of an individual or group to its environment or within the context of its environment. The term can refer generally to the way in which someone behaves or to an instance of such behavior.

behavioral genetics 1

The study of the relationship between genetic and environmental factors in accounting for individual differences of behavior.

bipolar disorder 5

A mood disorder characterized by swings from mania (exaggerated feeling of well-being) to depression, with a tendency to recur and subside spontaneously. Either the manic or the depressive episodes can predominate and produce mood swings, or the patterns of mood swings may be cyclical. The manic phase is characterized by elation, hyperactivity, over-involvement in activities, inflated self-esteem, a tendency to be easily distracted, and little need for sleep. The manic episodes may last from several days to months. In the depressive phase there is sluggishness (inertia), loss of self-esteem, withdrawal, sadness, and a risk of suicide.

candidate gene 2

A gene that has been hypothesized (often on the basis of animal studies) to have a causative effect on a phenotype.

causal pathway 6

The chain of events from cause to effect, such as from genotype and environments to phenotype.

chromosomes 2

The structures in an organism that contain an individual's genes. Humans typically have 46 chromosomes in every cell of their body, inheriting one of each chromosome in a pair from each parent. If a chromosome is missing, duplicated, or damaged, an individual can develop health problems.

cloning 4

A laboratory technique by which embryos are created using the complete DNA from the cell of one individual (as opposed to embryos that are created when a sperm and egg cell combine).

CODIS (Combined DNA Index System) 6

A searchable database of DNA profiles from convicted felons, operated by the Federal Bureau of Investigation (FBI).

cognition 1

The act or process of knowing, which includes awareness, judgment, perception, reasoning, and conceiving.

complex 5

Resulting from the expression of many different genes and the influence of many environmental factors.

concordance rate 4

The proportion of a sample of twin pairs that both have a particular trait.

consciousness 3

A sense of existence within a surrounding; a sense of being able to take action.

continuous trait 2

A trait that is measured on a continuous scale, for example, height. Synonym of quantitative trait. Antonym of discontinuous trait.

control group 4

A group of subjects in an experiment who do not have the trait under study or who are not given the experimental treatment under study.

correlation 2

An index of resemblance between two variables. Correlation also indicates resemblance between pairs of subjects such as twins, ranging from .0 for no resemblance to 1.0 for complete resemblance.

correlation coefficient 4

A number reflecting the extent to which scores on one variable can predict scores on a second variable.

criminality 6

The tendency to break the law, to be arrested, and/or to be convicted of a crime.

crossing over 4

See recombination.

cystic fibrosis 2

A disorder affecting the mucous lining of the lungs, leading to breathing problems and other health difficulties.

depression 1

A mental state characterized by low mood, low energy, and low enjoyment.

developmental noise 3

The variation introduced by minute, random events that occur during development and have a significant cumulative effect on the phenotype.

developmental pathway 3

The chain of events that occur over the course of an organism's development to produce its phenotype.

diploid 2

Having each chromosome in two copies per cell.

discontinuous trait 2

A trait that is either present or is not present. For example, a diagnosis of diabetes. Antonym of continuous trait.

DZ (dizygotic) 4

Resulting from two fertilized eggs occurring in the same womb at the same time, producing embryos that are roughly half identical (fraternal twins).

DNA (deoxyribonucleic acid) 2

The double-stranded molecule encoding the total genetic information of most organisms.

dominance 2

When one allele at a loci has overriding influence on the genotype relative to another allele at the loci.

dominant disorder 5

A disorder that can occur when either one or both of the alleles at a locus are mutations that improperly code for protein. Contrast with recessive disorder.

dopamine 6

A type of neurotransmitter.

early-onset Alzheimer's 2

A form of Alzheimer's disease that usually first appears in persons less than sixty-five years of age.

endophenotype 6

An intermediate trait that contributes to a phenotype. For example, capacity of working memory is an endophenotype of intelligence.

enhancement 6

The altering of a trait or set of traits to more desired forms.

envirome 3

The sum of all environmental influences surrounding and affecting a genome.

environment 1

The sum of circumstances, objects, and conditions that surround an individual. The aggregate of social, cultural, and physical environmental conditions that influence the life of an individual or community. For the gene, the environment encompasses all conditions external to the gene, including the influence of other genes.

environmentability 3

The phenotypic variation in a population that is due to environmental variation.

enzymes 2

Proteins that facilitate a biochemical reaction, usually speeding it up. Enzymes are essential for all forms of life.

epigenetic 2

When the action of a gene is affected without its DNA being altered.

epistasis 2

When an allele at one location in the genome affects the expression of another allele at another location.

equal environments assumption 4

The hypothesis that the environment of an identical twin pair does not work to make those two alike to any greater degree than the environment of a fraternal twin pair works to make those two alike.

ethnic 7

Describing a population of people that are related by blood and/or have common characteristics in terms of physical appearance, culture, religion, language, or nationality.

ethnicity

Common qualities or affiliation with large groups of people classed according to common racial, national, tribal, religious, linguistic, or cultural origin or background.

etiology 5

The pathway from initial cause to effects; the study of the origins of a phenomenon such as a disorder or behavioral trait.

eugenics 6

Philosophy and practice based on the belief that information about heredity can and should be used to improve the human race.

evolution 2

The process by which forms of life change over time because of variations in the DNA so that descendants differ from their predecessors.

factor analysis 7

Statistical methods that are used to reduce a large set of variables to the smallest number of factors that can account for individual differences in a trait.

family study 4

A type of research focusing on the phenotypic resemblance between genetically related members of a family. Through family studies, researchers estimate the extent to which resemblance is due to genetic or environmental factors.

first-degree relative 4

Parent, sibling, or child.

fragile X syndrome 5

The most commonly inherited form of mental retardation, which occurs in persons who have a gap (a "fragile site") on their X chromosome.

free will 6

The ability to make choices without undue influences present.

gamete 2

A sperm or egg cell, involved in reproduction.

gene/environment correlation 3

When individuals with a genetic propensity for a trait are in environments, or choose environments, that support expression of the trait.

gene/environment interaction 3

A situation in which the effect of a gene or genes depends on the type of environment to which it is exposed, or in which the effect of an environment depends on the presence of particular genes.

gene frequencies 4

The frequency of a particular allele at a locus in different population groups.

general cognitive ability (g) 6

A basic, core ability to make use of information. *g* is theorized to exist based on the observation that an individual's scores on different types of intelligence tests tend to correlate positively. A synonym is general intelligence factor.

genes 1

The hereditary units of life in chromosomes. Genes contain unique segments of DNA that provide the complete instructions for making the many proteins that are needed to create a unique individual.

gene therapy 5

An experimental procedure used to correct the harmful effects of a gene, sometimes by inserting a normal gene.

genetic determinism 2

The view that the development of an organism is determined solely by genetic factors. This view is not supported by science.

genetic drift 2

The change in allele frequencies within a species population over time due to chance.

genetic heterogeneity 5

When a trait or disorder can result from a mutated allele at any one of two or more loci. Also, when a trait or disorder can result from different mutations at the same locus (a synonym for this second definition is "allelic heterogeneity"). The term also is used to describe a population for which there are substantial differences among members with regard to their DNA sequences.

genetic marker 4

A DNA sequence at a known chromosomal site that shows variation in a population and is used in an association or linkage study.

genome 2

All the genetic material in the chromosome needed to create and maintain an organism.

genotype 2

Genetic makeup of an individual, or the combination of alleles relevant for a specific trait.

geotaxis 4

The tendency to move with or against gravity.

heredity 1

The sum of the qualities and potentialities genetically derived from one's ancestors, or the transmission of such qualities.

heritability 3

A term that describes the proportion of phenotypic variation among individuals in a specific population that can be attributed to genetic effects. Heritability is a characteristic of a population, not of an individual, and is an estimate of the relative importance of genetic influences on a trait (as opposed to environmental influences).

heterozygous 2

Having two alleles of a gene at a specific locus that are different.

homozygous 2

Having two alleles of a gene at a specific locus that are identical.

hormone 1

A blood-borne substance produced by glands that affects the metabolism or activity of certain other cells.

Human Genome Project 2

An international scientific collaboration that has resulted in the essentially complete sequencing (determining the order of all the bases) of the genome of humans and several other organisms.

Huntington's disease 2

A medical disorder resulting in progressive loss of cells in areas of the brain. It is caused by DNA changes on Chromosome 4. The disease typically appears in adulthood and leads to premature death.

imprinting 2

When an allele is expressed differently depending on whether it has been inherited from the mother (maternal imprinting) or the father (paternal imprinting).

impulsive behavior 4

An act performed in response to a stimulus without delay, reflection, voluntary direction, or obvious control.

impulsivity 6

The tendency to act without premeditation and forethought.

inbred strain 4

A population of a species in which all of its members are genetically alike. Inbred strains can be created by breeding siblings together over many generations until they are virtually alike genetically. This also can be accomplished through cloning.

injustice 6

Wrongful act or omission that denies an individual or group the benefits to which they have a rightful claim, or failure to distribute burdens in a fair manner.

insanity 6

A legal term indicating that a person committing a criminal act is unaware (due to a mental disorder) that the act is illegal.

intelligence 1

The ability to learn or understand, to deal with new or trying situations, or to use reason skillfully. Abilities associated with intelligence, such as application of knowledge to manipulate one's environment or thinking abstractly, are often measured by "objective" criteria (such as tests).

in vitro fertilization 7

The mixing of eggs with sperm in a laboratory dish in order to achieve conception. "In vitro" means "in glass."

IQ (intelligence quotient) tests 3

Assessments that require the completion of tasks designed to measure the trait of intelligence. Test scores are divided by chronological age to assign a numerical value (IQ) to the test-taker.

knockout study 4

A study of organisms (such as mice) whose genomes have been artificially manipulated to inactivate a particular gene. Any function that is subsequently altered usually may be assigned to the knocked-out gene.

linkage analysis 4

A procedure for determining the frequency with which two or more different genes are inherited together due to their proximity on a chromosome. This procedure is used to narrow down the location of a gene that contributes to a particular trait.

lobotomy 6

A surgical procedure in which an incision is made in the brain to reduce the transmission of nerve messages from one part of the brain to another and thus alter behavior.

locus 2

The position in a chromosome of a particular gene or allele.

lod score 4

The calculation of likelihood that a gene involved in one trait is close by on the same chromosome to a gene involved in another trait. Lod stands for "logarithm of the odds" or "likelihood of odds." A lod score above 3 indicates a likelihood by chance of 1/1000 and usually is considered "significant."

major gene 4

A gene for which allelic variations by themselves (apart from other genes and/or environmental influences) may be sufficient to trigger significant and easily observable differences in a trait.

manic-depressive illness 5

See bipolar disorder.

Mendelian 5

Based on the inheritance theories of Gregor Mendel, who discovered that certain simple traits are passed from generation to generation in dominant and recessive patterns.

mental illness 1

Refers collectively to diagnosable disorders of the brain. Mental disorders are characterized by abnormalities in cognition, emotion, or mood, or the highest integrative aspects of behavior, such as social interactions or planning of future activities.

meta-analysis 4

The pooling together of data from multiple independent studies in order to draw more broadly based findings.

microarray analysis 4

A technique to scan the activity of thousands of genes simultaneously.

microdeletion 5

A short sequence of an individual's DNA that is missing.

modifier gene 3

A gene that affects another gene, thereby altering the latter gene's effect on the phenotype.

molecular research 4

Studies at the biochemical level. In behavioral genetics, molecular research is typically directed at DNA and proteins and their interactions. For example, a molecular researcher may compare sections of the DNA sequences from multiple subjects and/or compare subjects' genotypes with observations of their phenotypes.

MZ (monozygotic) 4

Resulting from a single early embryo that splits to create two embryos (identical twins).

model fitting 4

An analytic process in which several mathematical models estimating the relative contributions of genetic and environmental factors to a trait are proposed. The models are compared, using standard statistical methods, to find the one that best explains the data.

mood disorders 1

Emotional behavior inappropriate for one's age or circumstances, characterized by, for example, unusual excitability or loss of energy, guilt, anxiety, or hostility.

multigenic 5

Resulting from the expression of many different genes. A synonym of polygenic.

multifactorial 5

Resulting from the expression of many different genes and the influence of many environmental factors.

multiple intelligences 6

The view that humans have several distinct kinds of abilities that enable them to solve problems; for example, linguistic ability, logical-mathematical ability, and more.

multiple locus gene of small effect 4

A gene whose alleles, operating in synchrony with alleles of other genes, contribute to variation in a trait.

mutation 2

A change, deletion, or rearrangement in an organism's DNA sequence when the mutation occurs in a gene, the protein-encoding message of that gene may be altered.

natural selection 2

The process by which members of a species have traits that enable them to take better advantage of their environment. Those with the advantageous traits leave more descendents for the next generation, so the trait itself may become more prevalent in the species.

nature v. nurture 3

The controversy over whether genetic inheritance (our innate nature) or environment (upbringing) determines behavior. Since both nature and nurture undoubtedly contribute to behavior, this 'either-or' thinking is not an accepted dichotomy by scientists.

negative eugenics 7

Practices (including, but not limited to, sterilization, incarceration, and killing) to discourage reproduction by persons whose characteristics are not desired in the next generation. Compare to positive eugenics.

nervous system 2

The brain, spine, and network of nerves. Information is communicated throughout the body via electrical and chemical transmission along the nervous system.

neurotransmitter 6

A chemical released by nerve endings to carry messages between nerve cells.

nonadditive 2

When an allele's contribution to the variation in a phenotype is affected by the presence of other alleles at the same locus or at a different loci. Antonym of additive.

nonshared environment 3

Environmental factors that contribute to differences among family members. Antonym of shared environment.

norm of reaction 6

The variety of phenotypes that result from a given genotype in each possible environment.

normal 5

Conforming to an expected, typical, or healthy behavior, pattern, or type. Antonym of pathological.

normal curve of distribution 6

Scores for a trait value that cluster around the middle of the distribution and are less frequent as the extremes are approached. This creates a "bell curve" when plotted on a graph. Most behavioral phenotypes show a normal curve of distribution.

novelty seeking 6

The tendency to seek out and enjoy novel, and sometimes risky, experiences.

nucleotide 2

A building block of DNA and RNA.

pathological 5

Not conforming to an expected, typical, or healthy behavior, pattern, or type. Also, compulsive or diseased. Antonym of normal.

pedigree 4

A family tree that indicates those who show a particular health or behavioral condition.

phenotype 2

The visible properties of an organism that are produced by the interaction of the genotype and the environment; also, any one trait or any group of traits.

PKU (phenylketonuria) 3

A medical disorder that, if untreated, often results in severe mental retardation. The body does not produce enough of a particular enzyme, leading to an excess of a compound that damages the brain.

pleiotropy 2

The ability of a gene to have multiple phenotypic effects, such as simultaneous effects on hair color, brain function, and motor control.

polygenic 5

Resulting from the expression of many different genes. A synonym of multigenic.

polypeptide chain 2

A series of hundreds or thousands of amino acids linked together. Proteins are formed when polypeptide chains (and sometimes shorter "peptide chains") join together into a three-dimensional structure.

population genetics 7

The study of those forces that affect gene frequencies.

positive eugenics 7

Practices (such as propaganda campaigns and rewards) to encourage reproduction by persons whose characteristics are desired in the next generation. Compare to negative eugenics.

pre-implantation diagnosis and selection 6

A medical procedure by which the DNA of embryos created through in vitro fertilization is analyzed for one or more disorders and/or traits; those without mutant alleles can be selected for implantation.

prenatal diagnosis 6

A medical procedure to determine the prospective health of a baby before it is born.

proband 4

The person that is the first subject to be identified in a study.

protein 2

Substances that consist of amino-acid residues joined by peptide bonds. Many essential biological compounds such as enzymes, hormones, or immunoglobulins are proteins.

QTL (quantitative trait locus) 2

One locus (gene) among many in the genome that affects a continuous trait.

QTL analysis 4

A type of molecular research that seeks the locations of the many genes whose alleles contribute to a variable trait.

quantitative genetic trait 2

A trait for which the observable phenotype associated with an underlying genotype varies across a population by measurable quantities or degrees, for example, height.

quantitative research 4

Studies of traits that vary quantitatively (that vary by degree in individuals in a population). Such studies are done by observing the phenotypes of subjects.

race 7

A classification of people on the basis of their pheno-typic characteristics that are presumed to be inherit-able. The notion of race as based on specific biological traits is not embraced by most scientists; however, race as a social variable is viewed as a topic meriting scientific investigation.

reaction range 6

See norm of reaction.

recessive disorder 5

A disorder that can occur only when both alleles at a locus are mutations that do not properly encode for protein. Contrast with dominant disorder.

recombination 4

When a section of one chromosome switches places with the same section from the other chromosome of a pair or with a section from another chromosome.

replication 5

A scientific research study that repeats or is very similar to an earlier study in order to confirm or disconfirm the earlier findings.

responsibility 6

The term has several meanings. To be "causally respon-sible" is to cause something to happen, either directly or indirectly. To be "legally responsible" is to be held accountable under the law and be subject to legal conse-quences for one's actions. To be "morally responsible" is to have a moral obligation, for which the fulfillment or failure to fulfill is deserving of praise or blame. In both morality and law, one's responsibility is judged in the context of the ability to understand the nature and con-sequences of one's actions and to control one's behavior.

RNA (ribonucleic acid) 2

A single-stranded nucleic acid that plays a central role in protein synthesis and gene regulation. RNA contains ribose, in contrast to the deoxyribose in DNA.

schizophrenia 1

A mental disorder characterized by disturbances in thought, personality, conscious awareness, sensation, and behavior.

second-degree relative 4

Aunt, uncle, grandchild, grandparent, niece, or nephew.

shared environment 3

Environmental factors that contribute to similarities among family members. Antonym of nonshared environ-ment.

sickle cell disease 6

A disorder in which red blood cells take on an unusual shape, leading to other blood and circulation problems.

SNP (single nucleotide polymorphism) 4

A single bit of DNA in a genome's sequence that varies among members of a species. Each bit is one base (nucleotide): either adenine (A), cytosine (C), thymine (T) or guanine (G).

stem cell 4

An undifferentiated cell. Those found in early embryos can mature into many different cell types, such as blood, bone, or neurons.

susceptibility gene 5

A gene whose alleles may increase or decrease one's probability of having or acquiring a trait or disorder.

tandem repeats 5

Multiple copies of the same base sequence that appear one after another in the genome.

thalassemia 6

A blood disease, occurring chiefly among people of Mediterranean descent, characterized by the production of abnormal hemoglobin. The word means "anemia of the sea."

twin study 4

A type of research in which the subjects are pairs of twins, identical or fraternal or both. In the study, each twin is identified as having or not having the trait/disorder under study; this information is used to establish a concordance rate for the trait. Often in such a study, concordance rates for fraternal and identical twins are obtained and compared.

violence 6

Rough, injurious or abusive physical force, action, or treatment, or an instance of such behavior.

whole genome scan 4

The search of a subject's entire genome that uses many genetic markers selected to sample segments of all the chromosomes. The markers may be segments of DNA and/or SNPs.

X-linked disorder or trait 5

A phenotype that results in part or whole from alleles at a locus on the X (sex) chromosome.

AAAS/HASTINGS CENTER BEHAVIORAL GENETICS PROJECT

Project Working Group Members

V. Elving Anderson, Ph.D., Professor Emeritus, Genetics and Cell Biology, University of Minnesota, Minneapolis, MN

Catherine Baker, M.A., Plain Language Communications, Bethesda, MD

Jonathan Beckwith, Ph.D., American Cancer Society Professor of Microbiology & Molecular Genetics, Department of Microbiology & Molecular Genetics, Harvard Medical School, Boston, MA

Dan W. Brock, Ph.D., Professor of Social Medicine and Director, Division of Medical Ethics, Harvard Medical School, MA

Audrey Chapman, Ph.D., Director, Science and Human Rights Program, American Association for the Advancement of Science, Washington, DC

Troy Duster, Ph.D., Director, Institute for the Study of Social Change, University of California, Berkeley, CA

Harold Edgar, LL.B., Julius Silver Professor of Law, Science & Technology, Columbia Law School, New York, NY

Lee Ehrman, Ph.D., Distinguished Professor of Biology, Division of Natural Sciences, Biology Program, State University of New York– Purchase, Purchase, NY

Leonard Fleck, Ph.D., Professor, Center for Ethics & Humanities, Michigan State University, East Lansing, MI

Mark S. Frankel, Ph.D., Director, Scientific Freedom, Responsibility and Law Program, American Association for the Advancement of Science, Washington, DC

Irving Gottesman, Ph.D., Sherrell J. Aston Professor of Psychology Emeritus, University of Virginia, Charlottesville, VA, and Bernstein Professor in Adult Psychiatry, University of Minnesota Medical School, Minneapolis, MN

Gregory Kaebnick, Ph.D., Editor, *Hastings Center Report* and Associate for Philosophical Studies, The Hastings Center, Garrison, NY

Patricia King, J.D., Carmack Waterhouse Professor of Law, Medicine, Ethics and Public Policy, The Law Center, Georgetown University, Washington, DC

Yvette Miller, M.D., Medical Director, American Red Cross, Tucson, AZ

Thomas H. Murray, Ph.D., President, The Hastings Center, Garrison, NY

Erik Parens, Ph.D., Associate for Philosophical Studies, The Hastings Center, Garrison, NY

Karen Porter, J.D., Scarsdale, NY

Nancy Press, Ph.D., Associate Professor, Department of Public Health and Preventative Medicine, Oregon Health Sciences University, Portland, OR

Kenneth F. Schaffner, M.D., Ph.D., University Professor of Medical Humanities, George Washington University, Washington, DC

Robert Wachbroit, Ph.D., Research Scholar, Institute for Philosophy & Public Policy, University of Maryland,College Park, MD

Rick Weiss, M.A., Science Writer, *Washington Post*, Washington, DC